CONTENTS

Introduction

Body Image is the twenty-fourth volume in the series: **Issues For The Nineties**. The aim of this series is to offer up-to-date information about important issues in our world.

Body Image looks at obesity, slimming, anorexia and bulimia. The information comes from a wide variety of sources and includes:

Government reports and statistics
Newspaper reports and features
Magazine articles and surveys
Literature from lobby groups
and charitable organisations.

It is hoped that, as you read about the many aspects of the issues explored in this book, you will critically evaluate the information presented. It is important that you decide whether you are being presented with facts or opinions. Does the writer give a biased or an unbiased report? If an opinion is being expressed, do you agree with the writer?

Body Image offers a useful starting-point for those who need convenient access to information about the many issues involved. However, it is only a starting-point. At the back of the book is a list of organisations which you may want to contact for further information.

*****

Editor

Craig Donnellan

Independence
Educational Publishers
Cambridge

First published by Independence
PO Box 295
Cambridge CB1 3XP

British Library Cataloguing in Publication Data
Body Image– (Issues for the Nineties Series)
I. Donnellan, Craig II. Series
646.7'5

ISBN 1 86168 003 1

Printed in Great Britain
at Leicester Printers Ltd
Leicester, Great Britain

Typeset by
Claire Boyd

Cover
The illustration on the front cover is by
Anthony Haythornthwaite / Folio Collective.

Are you a healthy weight?

Information from the Health Education Authority

Food provides energy (or calories) which our bodies need in order to work properly, for children to grow and for all of us to do everyday activities like walking, lifting, standing, gardening, cooking, etc. We take in energy as food and use it through physical activity. If the foods we eat provide more energy (calories) than we use up, then we will put on weight. This is a balancing act – sometimes the phrase 'energy balance' is used.

Energy can be measured in kilocalories (kcal) often referred to as calories, or kilojoules (kJ).

It is not healthy to be either underweight or overweight. If you don't eat enough food and you become underweight, you may not be getting all the nutrients you need from your diet. If, on the other hand, you eat more than you need and become overweight, you are more likely to suffer from problems such as heart disease, high blood pressure and diabetes.

Before you start a weight-reduction diet, check that you really do need to lose weight. If your weight is in the OK weight range, you do not need to lose weight or to restrict your energy (calorie) intake. It may result in your diet not supplying all the nutrients you will need. If you are in the lower end of the OK weight range, make sure you maintain your weight and don't be tempted to aim for the underweight category.

If you do need to lose weight, check with your doctor if you've had problems with your health in the past. Children, expectant and nursing mothers and those who are very fat have special needs and in these cases your doctor may refer you to a dietitian.

If you are overweight, you should make sure you do not gain any more weight. Try taking in less energy (calories) from food and doing more physical activity. Aim to lose half to one kilogram (one to two pounds) a week until you get down to the OK weight range. Then you should maintain your lower weight by following the healthy eating advice that is given throughout this booklet and by doing some regular physical activity. © Health Education Authority

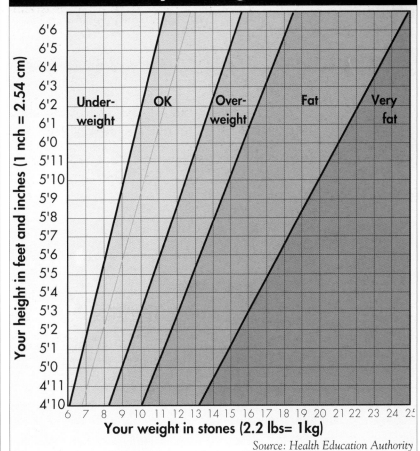

Are you the right weight for your height?

Underweight OK Overweight Fat Very fat

Your height in feet and inches (1 inch = 2.54 cm)

6'6 6'5 6'4 6'3 6'2 6'1 6'0 5'11 5'10 5'9 5'8 5'7 5'6 5'5 5'4 5'3 5'2 5'1 5'0 4'11 4'10

6 7 8 9 10 11 12 13 14 15 16 17 18 19 20 21 22 23 24 25

Your weight in stones (2.2 lbs= 1kg)

Source: Health Education Authority

Weight

Information from the Flora Project for Heart Disease Prevention

Being overweight – the problems

Being excessively overweight should be taken seriously. Next time you are in a supermarket, pick up a standard 1kg bag of sugar and weigh it in your hands. Many people are 13kgs overweight – try to imagine having to carry 13 bags around all day, everyday. You can see why being overweight can quite literally wear the body out.

Your heart has to work harder as your weight increases. As well as having more fat on their bodies, overweight people often have more fat in their blood which can lead to a build up of deposits in blood vessels increasing the risk of stroke and heart attack.

Joints can also suffer. Your body is designed to carry a certain weight. Just as your car springs will groan or snap with an overloaded boot, so joints will complain if asked to carry too much. In the long term, you could suffer from arthritis. Correct your weight and your joints will reward you with increased mobility. Many people who lose weight find their ease of movement increases dramatically.

There are many other health risks from being excessively over-weight – high blood pressure, stroke, diabetes, bronchitis and gallstones. But remember, the risk of suffering these complaints can fall dramatically if you can get nearer to your ideal weight.

Why do people put on weight?

Many believe that being overweight is a 'glandular' disturbance, but this is very rare. The truth is much simpler. You put on weight when energy intake exceeds energy output – when you eat and drink more than your body can use in your everyday activities.

People often assume that their emotional problems are the result of being overweight. This is sometimes true, but the opposite is more usual. Becoming excessively fat, or too thin, can be a way of expressing pent up anger. If you are eating because you are anxious, insecure, lonely, depressed or tense, once these stresses are reduced, weight loss often becomes much easier.

Whatever you do . . .

Don't turn to crash diets, appetite suppressants, or any other fads as these are only effective in the short term, and before long any weight lost will soon re-appear. Your aim is to re-work your lifestyle and eating and drinking habits . . . think long-term, rather than short-term. Your new food choices are for life and your shopping habits should change with them.

When you've succeeded

Once your weight is right and you've made new food choices to help maintain a healthy weight, you'll look trimmer and feel better. Your risk of serious illness will have been reduced along with the reading on the weighing scales. Your extra confidence and energy will have you wanting to improve in other areas of your life. Soon you will be taking on challenges that you would not have dreamt of before!

What you can do

Food

1. Eat three moderate meals a day rather than one large one and remember it's the type of foods you eat which are important not just the quantity. (For more information see the leaflet entitled 'Food Choices' in this series from the Flora Project).

2. Choose low-fat foods – grilled, steamed or poached – and eat less fatty fried foods such as chips, which should be kept for an occasional treat.

3. Use all fats, oils, spreads, margarines and butters as sparingly as possible. Choose a low-fat spread and make sure it's high in polyunsaturates.

4. Eat plenty of fresh vegetables and salads and choose fresh fruit instead of pudding.

5. Fibre-rich starchy foods like wholemeal bread and pasta,

jacket potatoes and high fibre breakfast cereals should be included in your diet as they help to satisfy your appetite without providing too many calories.

6. Drink plenty of fluids like water and low-calorie soft drinks, and cut down on alcohol which is high in calories.

7. Avoid sugar, sweets, crisps, cakes, biscuits, pastries and pies as these are all high in calories.

Exercise

1. The other side of balancing the weight equation, is regular, brisk exercise such as walking or swimming. It will help shed pounds and tune up the body's weight regulation system.

2. Use the stairs, not the lift. Say 'no' to a short bus or car ride – walk. Try a few sports, to find one you enjoy. (For more information see the leaflet entitled 'Fitness and Exercise' in this series from the Flora Project).

Dieting myths

There is a common misunderstanding that weight control can be accomplished overnight. Not surprising, with so many 'wonder diets' around.

Losing excess weight is a gradual process. You should aim to lose about

.5-1kg per week until you reach a weight which is ideal for your height and build. The most effective way to lose weight is by modifying your diet and taking regular exercise. To lose weight you will need to take in less energy (calories) than you burn up.

Many people think that to lose weight the sugar in their diet is the only thing that should be reduced. However, it is more important to reduce the amount of fat that you eat, whilst remembering that some is essential for good health so it should not be cut out altogether.

Being excessively overweight is not just a cosmetic problem – your health will suffer if you keep your weight higher than is ideal for you. Once you have reached your ideal weight you should continue to exercise and eat a well-balanced diet to maintain your ideal weight.

As a start, collect all six leaflets in this series and act today to give your heart a healthy boost. Look after it and it will look after you.

For more information contact:

The Flora Project for Heart Disease Prevention
24-28 Bloomsbury Way,
London WC1A 2PX
Tel: 0800 446464,
or any of the organisations listed below...

British Heart Foundation
14 Fitzhardinge Street,
London W1H 4DH

Health Education Authority
Hamilton House,
Mabledon Place,
London WC1H 9TX

ASH – Action on Smoking and Health
109 Gloucester Place,
London W1H 3PH

Fear of fat

How we feel about our body image is vital to our self-esteem, but is swinging from diet to diet the right course, or can we be happy with what we've got? Four women tell us how they feel . . .

Few women are immune to their own body image. So much so that almost a million of us paid up to be weighed and applauded at Weight Watchers last year.

'We've an incredibly wide variation in body weight,' says Dr Andrew Hill, Senior Lecturer in Behavioural Sciences at the University of Leeds. 'There are naturally thin and naturally fat people – those who eat like a horse and don't change weight, and those who only have to look at food to gain it. It has a lot to do with individual differences and the way the body handles food.'

Body image

The way we see ourselves is all about the way we feel. As Dr Hill explains: 'Self-liking is coloured by our own general self-esteem, the way people react to us, and how effectively we use those mental buffers we possess to suppress any negative comments people make.

'If you're really sensitive, you'll pick up on those negative comments and glances. But it is possible to push them to one side if you have good self-esteem and you're feeling strong. This usually means you'll get rewards from other areas in your life, too.

There's no reason why you should be a slave to your outside appearance – what's inside is what is important.

'For some people, their body shape will never be satisfactory, so they need to divert their attentions and efforts towards being good at something else, such as a hobby, job or sport. Finding self-worth and fulfilment is the key to happiness.'

The successful slimmer

Iona Woolgrove, 24, a fashion supervisor from Andover
'My nickname at school was Earthquake,' recalls Iona. 'I was a fat

child and, of course, it upset me but I always tried to pretend that it didn't.

'What mattered more, though, and still matters now, is my brother Alistair's nickname for me – Fats!

'Mum was always dieting – without success – so I was told not to eat this and that. But it had the opposite effect and I ate more.'

At 15, Iona was a size 18. Despite sporadic attempts to diet, she remained a fat teenager. 'Inside I wished I was slim, but it didn't really affect my social life as I was growing up.' By 21, when she landed her first job as a part-time lecturer, Iona had ballooned to 14 stone 7lbs: 'There were comments, but I was sick of being told to lose weight.'

Then in 1994, she met her boyfriend Paul: 'I was big, about 12 stone 7lbs, yet it didn't seem to worry him. When I was invited to be a bridesmaid in St Lucia at his brother's wedding, though, I panicked. No way was I going to look like a beached whale next to the slim, pretty bride!'

Iona went to a slimming club and, in just four months, reached her target weight of 9 stone 7lb: 'I cried when the scales tipped that magic goal. I felt so confident at the wedding and even lying on the beach. I just regret all those years I spent being fat. No way will I ever be big again.'

And now . . .
At 5ft 5in, Iona is a perfect size 12: 'My self-esteem is better, but I'm still vulnerable if I have a bad day at work – I have to check the mirror and reassure myself that those days are gone for ever.'

The yo-yo dieter
Tanya Hassey, 31, from Oakridge, works part time
Tanya's weight problem first started during her childhood: 'I was always a bit chubby,' recalls Tanya. 'I come from a hearty eating family where Mum was always in the kitchen making cakes – in fact, they were the first things I learned how to cook.'

Tanya, now in her second marriage to Tony, is mum to Natasha, 11, Diane, 10, Elvin, six, and Leah, five. At 17, she wore a size 12, weighing just over nine stone. But by 19 she was married and pregnant, and her weight shot up. Then she

---

Fat facts

- Eighty-five per cent of British women would like to lose weight

- An estimated one-third of the British population is dieting at any given time.

- Sales of diet foods in the UK totalled £45 million in 1995.

- Dieting can make you forgetful – of the 300 people given mental tests by the Institute of Food Research, the slimmers scored the lowest marks.

---

had her second child and, despite losing weight initially after the birth, within a few months her weight had soared to 11 stone 4lb. By the time Diane, her second child, was two and a half, Tanya was up to 12 stone 6lbs. Her marriage broke up about this time, too.

Within a year, however, she'd lost weight and was a size 12 again. Then she met her second husband, Tony: 'Life together was too comfortable and I went up to 11 stone 4lb and a size 16. Tony didn't really notice, but it did bother me.' Two more children came along and Tanya got bigger: 'I grew into a size 18. Then I started going on diets and breaking them. I did manage to get down to a size 14 in 1994.'

Just like other yo-yo dieters who go on and off diets all the time, Tanya discovered that each time she lost weight and regained it, she put on a few extra pounds on top . . .

This happens because dieting slows down the body's metabolism as the body gets used to a lower calorie intake. When you regain weight, the new weight is more likely to be made of fat than muscle. And, as fat uses up far fewer calories than muscle, you need less calories to remain the same weight.

And now . . .
Tanya weighs 11 stone: 'When I look in the mirror I see the truth – I think my bum and stomach are too big. Also, no matter how slim I get, I still feel fat inside.'

The woman who thinks she's fat
Sally Neilson, 39, a community carer from Bookham
Sally Neilson is in her second marriage to a man almost 10 years her junior. She has four children and works six days each week caring for disabled people. At 5ft 4in, she is a petite size 10 to 12 – but she genuinely believes she is fat.

'When I look in the mirror I see a horrible shape – I see an old hag,' explains Sally, who seems to have a morbid fear of getting fat: 'I couldn't handle being fat, and I'd be afraid of how others would see me – in fact, I'm afraid of that already, so I don't weigh myself now.'

The fear of being overweight goes back to Sally's teenage years: 'When I was 18, I was happy with the way I looked – I was a size 12-14. Then I got engaged to a man who hardly ate and had a 26in waist. I started feeling fat and then stopped eating. Eventually I lost so much weight that I ended up in the hospital. I suppose it was anorexia.'

Once out of hospital, she stayed thin and says, 'I felt great, and I thought I looked lovely and slim. I'd still love to be skin and bone, but with everything in the right place. Friends always tell me I look nice, but I don't believe them. I think people just say that to be nice to me.'

Sally admits she has low self-esteem and acknowledges her job as a community carer helps improve her self-confidence: 'The people that I look after really appreciate me and I like that feeling.'

And now . . .
Eating, for Sally, is a guilt-ridden experience: 'I never go on a diet, but I only eat once a day in the evening. If I have two meals during the day I feel really bad.'

Sally worries she might pass her fears on to her children: 'I buy lots of food and make the children eat. I don't want them to be like me. Debbie, my eldest daughter, is 14 and always says to me: "For God's sake, Mum, you're so skinny!" But she worries me because she also thinks she's fat, even though I keep telling her she's not.'

The overweight woman who's totally happy

Sally Date, 35, a mother of three from Popley

Totally at ease with her shape, Sally Date is divorced and has three children, Emma, who's 10, Christopher, seven, and Jonathan, five. She is now living with her new partner Henry.

'I was always big,' says Sally. 'All my family are tall and I'm big boned. Mum and Dad were always on diets, but somehow dieting never bothered me. I didn't see myself as fat – just tall. I put on a lot of weight in my teens and I went up to a size 18. Nobody commented on my weight. Perhaps I look as though I might say something back to them!'

After leaving university, Sally went to the States for a couple of years: 'During the first nine months there, I put on about three stone – that made me 15 stone.'

So Sally embarked on a totally drastic regime of coffee and Diet Coke: 'Then a friend told me I looked dreadful – really gaunt – and I don't want to look like that!'

Sally married at 24, and after she had her first child Emma, her weight soared up to a size 26: 'I didn't feel bad about it, I just love good food and eating out. Then I had Christopher, followed by Jonathan, and I was a little lighter after those two. I did get the odd hint from the Well Woman Clinic who said: "Do you realise you're overweight?" I just replied "Yes I do".

'I'm perfectly comfortable with

Body language

Your basic body shape will never change, despite diets or exercise, so try to come to terms with yours.
Endomorphs are solid, curvy and gain weight easily, but can usually carry it off.
Ectomorphs are seldom overweight and are often underweight, yet eat a lot.
Mesomorphs have a strong, feminine body with broad shoulders, a full bust and strong legs.

my size. I know I'm never going to be a size 12 or 14, so why should I worry? I'm a very happy go lucky person and I'm not worried about what other people think.

'If I did hear negative comments about me, my attitude would be, if you don't like it, don't look! I would worry, however, if my hair looked a mess or my clothes weren't nice. I always try to make an effort to look good.'

And now . . .
Sally currently wears a size 22-24 and is 5ft 10in tall: 'If someone said I could wake up tomorrow as a size 12, I wouldn't want it. It would change my life and the way other people saw me. I am who I am. And if I did slim down to a size 12, I'd be terrified of eating again.'

All in the mind

According to Dr Hill, big women fall into two categories: those who are immune to their body image and are perfectly happy to be big; and those who are unhappy about their size. The University of Leeds recently published a study of body-weight perceptions:

Children: The common view among nine-year-olds was that fat children had fewer friends, were less liked by their parents and even did less well in school.

Adults: The average-weight adult has a stereotypical perception of fat people – it seems they believe fat people are greedy, lazy, smelly, stupid and unhealthy.

Dr Hill sums it up: 'We are fatter than 10 years ago, but fat has become a modern three letter "F" word.'

Getting help

National Centre For Eating Disorders
The centre was founded by psychologist Deanne Jade in 1985. Her task was to educate people about the nature of their suffering – e.g. bulimics might have a treatable emotional disorder, not simply a deficit of willpower.

Today, the NCFED employs 18 trained counsellors and the network is expanding via regional centres with affiliated counsellors, and personal and telephone counselling. Call 01372 469493 for further information.
Eating Disorders Association
This is a charity set up to help sufferers and their families. See page 39 for address details.

© Essentials
April, 1996

Your ideal weight

What the charts don't tell you

The last time I saw my friend Joanne, I couldn't believe how much weight she'd lost. After a year abroad she was trim, slim and in superb shape. She'd become a fitness fanatic and looked a stone lighter. So it came as a real surprise when she said she hadn't lost any weight at all. In fact, she'd put on 7lb.

Fitness clichés are pretty meaningless until you see them in practice – but here was living proof that muscle weighs more than fat. Joanne weighs more – but is in much better shape than when she was half a stone lighter.

Which prompts the question – how do you determine your ideal weight? To rely on your scales clearly isn't enough. But let's face it, most of us do. Anyway, we all grew up with height/weight charts so there can't be many of us who don't have some idea of what we 'ought' to weigh.

The first height/weight chart appeared in 1959 and was based on the results of a huge survey carried out by the American insurance company Metropolitan Life. Ideal weights were based on people (all of whom were taking out insurance) who lived the longest, and for years all height/weight charts were based on this data.

The chart used today (by organisations such as the Health Education Authority) is the 'Garrow', devised by Professor John Garrow in 1981. The Garrow differs from previous charts in that it also takes into account Body Mass Index (BMI), and applies to both men and women. 'The chart works for both sexes, because research has shown that women can afford to put on more weight than men before they're exposed to the same health risks,' says Professor Garrow.

To calculate your body mass index:

Simply take your weight in kilograms and divide it by your height in metres squared.

E.g. a person who weighs 61.8kg (9st 10lb) and is 1.68m (5ft 6in) tall – 61.8 divided by 1.68^2 =21.9 BMI.

A BMI of:
- 20-25 = ideal
- 25-30 = overweight
- 30-40 = clinically obese
- 40+ = morbidly obese

The Garrow Chart gives you ideal weight as a range (usually about a stone), not a specific weight. Realistically, it isn't as strict as previous charts but falls within all the current recommendations for a healthy weight. According to Garrow, 'The original chart was too strict because it only took into consideration a very limited range of people – business types who were taking out insurance. More recent surveys have concentrated on a much wider section of people.'

Which group are you in?

To find out whether you're underweight, healthy or overweight, first find your height, then run your finger down to your present weight (only a small section of the chart is shown).

'If you're within the desirable range, you're okay,' says Garrow. 'There are currently lots of people who worry too much about their weight. The aim of this chart is to get them to stop worrying.'

According to Dr Carolyn Sumerbell of The London Hospital, 'If you fall into your ideal range then you'd do well to stay there, because research shows that as people get older they put on weight. So if you already fall into the overweight range, you risk getting even bigger. The more weight you carry, the worse it is for your health.'

Waist-fat test

A new test devised by Professors Lean and Ham at the University of Glasgow concentrates on the abdominal area. 'The amount of fat you carry on your tummy is the best indication of whether you are carrying too much fat,' says Professor Mike Lean. The waist test pinpoints two levels:

Action level 1 – Ideally women should have a maximum waist of no more than 80cm and men no more than 94cm. No matter what you weigh, to maintain good health you should try not to go above this waist size.

Action level 2 – However, if your waist measures more than 88cm, or 102cm, if you're a man, then you're putting your long-term health at risk and perhaps it's time to rethink your lifestyle.

© New Woman
January, 1996

Height (METRES) 2.54cm = 1 inch

Weight (KILOGRAMS) 1kg = 2.2lbs

Weight	1.52		1.56		1.60		1.64		1.68		1.72		1.76		1.80	
71	31	30	29	28	28	27	26	26	25	25	24	23	23	22	22
70	30	30	29	28	27	27	26	25	25	24	24	23	23	22	22
69	30	29	28	28	27	26	26	25	24	24	23	23	22	22	21
68	29	29	28	27	27	26	25	25	24	24	23	23	22	22	21	21
67	29	28	28	27	26	26	25	24	24	23	23	22	22	21	21
66	29	28	27	26	26	25	25	24	23	23	22	22	21	21	20
65	28	27	27	26	25	25	24	24	23	22	22	21	21	21	20
64	28	27	26	26	25	24	24	23	23	22	22	21	21	20	20
63	27	27	26	25	25	24	23	23	22	22	21	21	20	20	19
62	27	26	25	25	24	24	23	22	22	21	21	20	20	20	19
61	26	26	25	24	24	23	23	22	22	21	21	20	20	19	19
60	26	25	25	24	23	23	22	22	21	21	20	20	19	19	19
59	26	25	24	24	23	22	22	21	21	20	20	19	19	19	18
58	25	24	24	23	23	22	22	21	20	20	19	19	19	18	18
57	25	24	23	23	22	22	21	21	20	20	19	19	18	18	18
56	24	24	23	22	22	21	21	20	20	19	19	18	18	18	17
55	24	23	23	22	22	21	20	20	19	19	19	18	18	17	17
54	23	23	22	22	21	21	20	20	19	19	18	18	17	17	17

Overweight | Healthy | Underweight

Call for radical rethink on treatment of obesity

By Celia Hall,
Medical Editor

A worldwide campaign to stop millions of people becoming dangerously fat was launched by the World Health Organisation yesterday amid warnings that existing treatment methods were failing to stop an epidemic of obesity.

Prof Philip James, the chairman of the WHO International Obesity Task Force, called for a radical rethink on treating the problem.

He estimated that one in 20 obese Britons would be candidates for taking new types of slimming drugs permanently and that, for some, surgery would have to be considered.

'The major problem is that although people have been talking about obesity for a very long time, there is chaos in the field with most medical people not perceiving it as a disease,' said Prof James, a nutrition expert and director of the Rowett Research Institute, Aberdeen.

But he stressed that medical treatment was for obesity and not a cosmetic aid for slimmers. He said 'if that is what is required medically' there was no reason why people could not be kept on drugs indefinitely.

'The thinking that people are to blame for their own obesity is the key thing that needs to change.

'This is a medical condition where individuals are susceptible for a variety of reasons. So we have to get away from the victim-blaming business.

'The people who constantly say it is all a matter of self-control neglect all the chemistry and biology we are now beginning to understand.

'They are usually the thin people who actually never have to think about staying thin – they just have the right chemistry.'

Appetite suppressants are available but doctors prescribe them only until weight has been lost.

'That is mad – you would never take a diabetic or someone with high blood pressure off their drugs once you brought them down to normal,' said Prof James.

Two new types of drugs would be available in about three years' time, he said. One inhibits the way the body absorbs fat; the other is a new type of appetite suppressant which slightly changes the metabolism.

Surgery reducing the size of the stomach had shown good results, he added.

In Britain the number of men and women classed as obese rose by 15 per cent between 1980 and 1993. About 46 per cent of women and 56 per cent of men were overweight or obese at the end of 1993. Numbers continue to rise.

Doctors measure obesity by a body mass index which is the calculation of weight in kilograms divided by height squared. An index of 30 or more is obese.

In America it has been estimated that the entire population will be obese by 2230 if trends continue.

The WHO says that severe obesity is associated with a 12-fold risk of death in 25 to 35-year-olds.

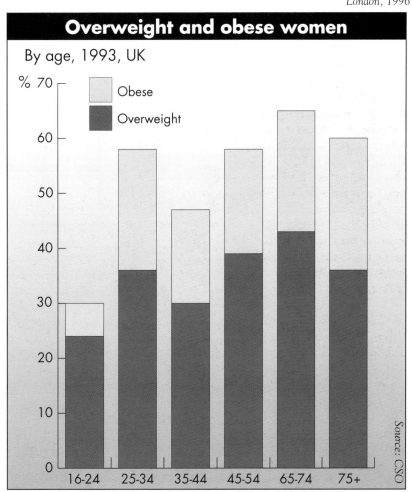

Overweight and obese women

By age, 1993, UK

Source: CSO

Attention all dieters: now you can eat what you like

Out: extreme diets and fad foods. In: potatoes, pasta and chocolate. The secret of healthy eating, argues Janette Marshall, lies in a balanced menu. And below, Annabel Ferriman meets two food lovers who make their own rules

Is your food intake anything like this? Thirty-four per cent bread, potatoes, pasta and other cereals (especially whole grain or high fibre types); 33 per cent vegetables and fruit (a wide variety but especially dark green and orange-coloured produce); 15 per cent milk, cheese, yogurt (lower fat varieties); 12 per cent meat, fish and alternatives (lower fat versions); 7 per cent fatty and sugary foods (fats should include minimal amounts of poly- or mono-unsaturated vegetable oils, margarine/spread and low fat spread, plus 'extras' such as crisps, chocolate, fizzy drinks, takeaways).

If the answer is yes, congratulations. According to current thinking, your diet is perfectly balanced.

If not, perhaps you are a reflection of the statistic which finds that despite consuming fewer calories than 20 years ago, more people are overweight than ever before. Traditional health messages to reduce fat, sugar and salt and increase fibre in the diet have apparently failed: we are still eating too much fatty and sugary food (as well as not taking enough exercise).

But there is good news. A more permissive attitude to food and diet has replaced the 'thou shalt not' approach of the 1980s. The new doctrine is that we can eat anything we like – as the breakdown illustrates – as long as we get the proportions right and take account of age and activity levels.

This balance is suitable for everyone from school age upwards. It helps to control weight and includes 'nutrient dense' foods with high levels of the vitamins, minerals, unsaturated fats and anti-oxidants that protect against heart disease,

cancer and other diseases associated with Western diets. Treats such as cakes, biscuits and chocolate can still be enjoyed but not eaten in such quantities, there is a danger that their 'empty calories' replace those of more nourishing foods. Those with a sweet tooth should stick to cereals, fruitcake and wholemeal fruited scones or hot cross buns, all of which are packed with vitamins and minerals.

The real trick is to eat the amount needed to suit age and activity level. Schoolchildren and teenagers, for example, often need to eat up to double the amount of adults to fuel growth spurts. Adults need to cut down on 'extras' such as alcohol, especially if they are sedentary. People over 50 may need to reduce the amount eaten as they become less active, or eat smaller amounts more frequently.

A more permissive attitude to food and diet has replaced the 'thou shalt not' approach of the 1980s

---

Other nutritional niceties affect different ages. Teenagers who replace meals with chocolate, chips, crisps, biscuits, cakes, takeaways and fizzy drinks are eating too much fat and have low vitamin and mineral intakes. Fertile women need to consider folic acid supplements, 400 micrograms (400ug/0.4mg) daily, and eat foods rich in folates such as green leafy vegetables, pulses, yeast extract, kidney, fortified bread and breakfast cereals. After the menopause, women lose the protective effect of hormones

against heart disease and osteoporosis, so they should increase calcium intake and reduce fat, although both are most effective done throughout life.

A typical day's healthy eating
Teenagers

Breakfast: fruit juice, fortified breakfast cereal with milk. If they won't eat breakfast, give them a wholemeal scone to take to school.

Mid-morning snack: fruitcake or cereal bar.

Lunch: baked potato with beans (or chilli or meat/fish/cheese), plus salad, followed by fruit/yogurt.

Teatime snack: breakfast cereal (if not eaten earlier), or sandwich(es).

Evening meal: Shepherd's pie made with lamb mince or vegetarian equivalent with two servings of vegetables and extra potato, if hungry. Pudding: choose from fruit salad, rice pudding with added fruit, bread and butter pudding, fruit fools or brûlés, fruit tarts.

Evening snack: milk shake or yogurt or fruit or toast.

Adults (age 18 plus)

Breakfast: fruit juice, breakfast cereal with milk and fresh fruit. If desired, wholemeal toast with low-fat spread or small amount of preserves.

Mid-morning snack (if required): fresh fruit/hot cross bun.

Lunch: sandwiches of lean meat/fish/cheese, with generous amount of salad, humus or peanut butter mixed with grated carrot or mashed banana. Salad on the side, if possible. Yogurt/fromage frais and/or fresh fruit. Fresh fruit juice or milk shake or drinking yogurt.

Dinner/main: fish (oily once/twice a week), lean meat or vegetarian equivalent with generous portion of (low-fat) potatoes/pasta/rice/bread and two servings of vegetables. Puddings: see above.

Adults (50 plus)
Breakfast: fruit juice, wholewheat or high-fibre breakfast cereal (don't add bran, it reduces mineral absorption) with milk and sliced banana/prunes.
Lunch (main meal): grilled or baked mackerel with potatoes or rice, peas and beans. Pudding: fruit crumble and custard made with semi-skimmed milk.
Teatime: fruit loaf or wholemeal toast.
Supper: cheese, bread/biscuits (no spread), fresh fruit, glass of milk. Leave 30 minutes after a meal before having a cup of tea to reduce iron loss and drink lots of fluid (water, fruit juice as well as tea/coffee and alternatives) as thirst diminishes with age.

The daily diet of a wholefood devotee

Christine Ayre's four-year-old daughter, Emily, thinks that the word pudding means yoghurt. She once had a chocolate mousse but she did not want to eat it all because it was 'too rich'.

The family eat vegetarian, organically grown wholefood with no added salt and drink filtered water and unsweetened fruit juices. Christine, who is a 36-year-old graphic designer, and her husband, John, who runs a wholefood shop, believe that they have educated their children's palates not to crave the heightened, artificial flavours of processed food.

'You are partly what you eat,' says Christine. 'With organic whole-food, you know you are not eating chemicals.

It is good, unprocessed food, untampered with, and as nature intended. We occasionally eat fish, but never touch meat or chicken.

'I have a great sense of well-being and feel in control of my health. I rely on it to see me through. With work and two small children, I lead a very busy life. If you are worn out and cross all the time, it is not fair to them.'

Christine and John first became vegetarian when they were students

IT ALL STARTED WHEN HE CHANGED FROM WHITE TO BROWN BREAD

KenPyne

at York University and extremely hard-up. 'We took it up because it was cheap,' she says. They read Rose Elliott's *The Bean Book*, which educated them about wholefood. 'Our eating is firmly rooted in the English wholefood tradition.'

Despite consuming fewer calories than 20 years ago, more people are overweight than ever before

---

Christine starts the day with a bowl of muesli and soya milk, while the children, Emily, four, and Harriet, three, eat various cereals from their father's shop with added fresh fruit. For lunch, Christine eats a salad from the local supermarket, often tabbouleh, with bean salad and some green leaves.

For supper, she first decides whether to have pasta, bread, potatoes or rice and then decides what to put with it. The evening I saw her, her children had chosen to have pasta, so she had made a cheese sauce and steamed some small green beans to go with it. Everyone liked it. She always makes too much, so the children can take the leftovers to school the next day.

If they eat rice, John usually makes stir-fried vegetables and tofu, and if they eat baked potatoes, they will usually have butter, cheese or

baked beans with them. They always have green vegetables as well. In the winter, they eat a lot of home-made vegetable soup and toast.

Christine admits there are two problems about eating the way they do: the cost and the time. 'I am lucky because almost all our food comes from my husband's shop, but for some people the price of fresh, organic produce can be prohibitive.

'This kind of cooking can also be rather labour intensive, which is why I often cook in bulk, making too much, so that the children can have the leftovers the next day. Sometimes I put potatoes in the oven before I go out in the morning and set the oven to come on before we get home, so supper is almost ready when we get in.'

The couple, who live in Kentish Town, north London, do not believe in forbidding their children things because they think that makes them more attractive. So they were allowed chocolate Easter eggs and they have eaten at McDonald's.

'I have probably taken them twice. They have eaten the chips and drunk fresh orange juice. But I do not like their food. You do not know where it comes from. It just arrives in huge lorries. And their rolls are a travesty of bread.'

Christine says the whole family is extremely healthy. 'I would not put it all down to the food, since John and I both come from very healthy families, but the food stands you in good stead.'

Confessions of a fast food fanatic

If you glance inside Phil Treseder's car, you get a pretty good picture of his diet. It is full of empty crisp packets, chocolate bar wrappers, sandwich bags and tins of Coca-Cola.

Treseder, a 33-year-old children's rights consultant, reckons he eats about one healthy meal a week. 'I share the house with some vegetarians and we sometimes eat a meal together at weekends. Otherwise, I am afraid it is takeaways for me: chips, pizzas and Chinese.'

Weighing in at about 15 stone ('I don't know exactly because I don't have any scales'), he blames his work for his diet. 'I travel a great deal, so I don't buy much fresh food, because it goes off before I have a chance to eat it.

'I probably have vegetables about once a week, and fruit twice a week. I am not a great fan of either. I go to the pub two or three times during the week and drink about two pints, but at the weekends when I go,

I drink five or six pints each night. When I went to the rugby international in Dublin recently, I hate to think how much I drank, because we just drank all the time. Then again, if I am running a residential course for kids I won't drink anything at all.'

For breakfast, he has toast (brown or white, according to what the shop has in stock) with jam or marmalade and tea. If he is at home for lunch he will have another round of toast with cheese or taramasalata. If he is out, it is a sandwich or a couple of pasties. Supper is either a takeaway, such as a spicy chicken or pepperoni pizza, or, at home, it is a fried egg or beans on toast. He drinks about seven or eight cups of tea and really strong coffee a day, with semi-skimmed milk.

'I have never had any serious illnesses. Occasionally I have tonsillitis and I had chickenpox as an adult, but that obviously is not connected to my diet,' Phil says. 'I am probably half a stone overweight,

because although I am about 15 stone, I am tall (6ft 3in).

'My only health problem is an allergy to the house dust mite, for which I take antihistamines, and which I could probably control by cutting down on dairy products. I went to a homeopath about it once, who gave me some stuff to take, but told me that I could not take it if I drank coffee. I thought "no chance".

'I am pretty contented and do not intend to change my diet. I know that a healthy diet contains lots of fresh fruit and vegetables and fewer dairy products than I eat and I would like to see healthy eating encouraged. I am quite convinced that a lot of cancer is linked to diet and I mistrust the food industry and the Government, because they do not inform the public properly.

'I can see strong reasons to change my diet, but it is not practical. I am too tied up in my work to worry about it, or to be able to change it.'

© The Independent
May, 1996

Slim chance . . .

Even the 'experts' can get it wrong, says Elizabeth Wilson

If you've ever lived with someone on the Scarsdale diet (or even inflicted it upon yourself), then you'll already know the score. I shared a flat with a woman (let's call her 'Jane') who dieted for two weeks in every six, subsisting on one grapefruit for breakfast, two hard-boiled eggs for lunch, and a sad little steak with (whoopee!) a green salad for dinner. I say two weeks in every six because, inevitably, the minute she started eating anything reasonably pleasurable, she gained weight and the whole gruesome process began again. To this day, the sight of two boiled eggs gurgling in a pan of boiling water fills me with vague feelings of irritation.

In vain did we, her flatmates, wave magazine features under Jane's nose trumpeting that she was hopelessly out of date. Pasta was OK,

bread could be eaten in moderation, yes, even the odd glass of wine wouldn't mean exile to the Big Girls' department. It had no effect whatsoever.

The shelves groan with 'lite, lo-fat, no-fat' products. But are they too good to be true?

We may have been living in the 80s but, when it came to dieting, Jane was firmly planted in the early 70s. Her mother was an aficionado of the Scarsdale diet and Jane had grown up in a household where the word 'diet' meant high protein –

despite the fact that its developer, Dr Herman Tarnower, was murdered by his lover, which ought to have told her something.

But it isn't just the high protein proponents who get it wrong. As a teenager in the 70s, I was much taken by one of the first magazine articles to promote a high-fibre regime. In those days, fibre was almost invisible in the Great British Diet. This explained, said the article, why we suffered disproportionately from heart disease, cancer and a host of other ills.

Apparently, the solution was to eat bran. So, to the vast amusement of my family, I started shovelling bran down my throat with every meal. Very dry and nasty it was, too.

Yes, I was on the right track, but bran in its constituted form is not the way to up your fibre – I now know that an excessive amount hinders the absorption of vitamins. Given the quantities I consumed in my formative years, it's incredible I didn't develop scurvy.

I still wonder how many women around the country, who started on the bran path to salvation with me, are still forcing it down and wondering why their hair is falling out.

Our concern now is lowering fat levels. We are advised to get no more than 30% of our daily calorie intake from fat. Ironically, the US, land of the larger-than-life, is moving towards 20%.

The shelves groan with 'lite, lo-fat, no-fat' products. But are they too good to be true? The trouble with cutting down fat is that research has shown that it is the calories from fat that make food appetising. We may be full, but we won't necessarily be satisfied, and that could lead us to overeat.

The latest dietary advice is to forget about calories, and concentrate on cutting down on fat, but even then results aren't guaranteed. One woman who tried this method admitted she felt better but wasn't losing any weight. When she examined her diet, she discovered she was eating about 700 calories of muesli at breakfast alone! 'The truth is, I'm just greedy,' she moaned. 'It doesn't really matter what kind of food you have, if you put food away like I do, you're going to stay fat.' Perhaps we'll get to the stage where we just don't care. Trend forecasters predict that, after a decade of excessive body consciousness, we're going to recover our enthusiasm for living well – 'eat, drink and be merry' and to hell with Weight-Watchers.

1918 – The calorie is born
'You have known only in a dumb despairing sort of way that all the foods you like are fattening, and that you must avoid them as a pestilence.' These were the words of Lulu Hunt, the American responsible for bringing the calorie out of the chemistry lab and into our homes. She recommended a surprisingly modern regime: 1,200 calories a day, low in fat, high in carbohydrates.

1930s – Fine if you like eggs
The Hollywood 18-day diet was developed for movie stars needing to lose weight fast. It advocated 585 calories a day, consisting of grapefruit and boiled eggs.

1950s & 60s – Taking protein too far
The deification of the boiled egg continued. This was when the high-protein lobby really came into its own. Gayelord Hauser promised you would *look younger, live longer* if you ate little more than steak and, you guessed it, hard-boiled eggs.

With the publication of Dr Herman Taller's diet in 1961, the protein proponents achieved their apotheosis. Dr Taller recommended at least a pound of meat on a daily basis and for those who were serious about losing weight (hold on to your crudités), a fat consumption of 65%, with only five per cent of calories derived from carbohydrates.

The latest dietary advice is to forget about calories, and concentrate on cutting down on fat, but even then results aren't guaranteed

---

It was another Herman, Dr Herman Tarnower, who developed what was to become the Scarsdale diet, which by the early 70s had begun to resemble a cult. Devotees tested their urine to check that they were 'ketosing' – breaking down fat properly.

1970s – all change to fibre
The Pritikin diet gained many devotees because it promised to reduce heart disease and hypertension. It recommended that 80% of energy is drawn from carbohydrates, and only about five per cent from fat – the war against cholesterol was on.

1980s & 90s – Appliance of science
Dieting hit fever pitch in the 80s.

America's *Shape* magazine quotes one survey that shows the number of articles on dieting in 22 magazines soared from 60 in the whole of 1979, to 66 in the first month of 1980 alone.

In 1990, Dr Dean Ornish became the guru of nutrition following his extensive study showing how a low-fat, vegetarian diet reduced the risk of heart disease. An important part of the programme was meditation and gentle exercise. Like everything else in the 90s, dieting has become 'touchy-feely' with the emphasis placed on the mind-body connection.

In 1993, the diet that the Sunday papers were waving their cheque books to get hold of came from Frenchman Michel Montignac. The key to his popularity was his claim that you could stay slim by pigging out on foie gras, cheese and chocolate, just like the French. His scientific theory was a little hard to get your head around, but who cared when his diet allowed you to drink red wine – if you were prepared to forgo carrots (for some reason, carrots were devil food to Montignac). But he may have been something of a pioneer because, as we approach the end of the 90s, it looks as if pleasure is back in vogue. Olestra, the 'king' of low-fat foods, has been licensed for use in the US in crisps and tortilla chips, with more products to follow.

Olestra tastes like fat but passes through the body without settling on your hips. It is a 'fabricated food' and medics in the US have been concerned by reports that, in its passage through the gut, it leaches important minerals and vitamins.

The manufacturers claim to have sorted this out – along with other side-effects such as flatulence, stomach cramps and 'anal leakage'.

But with or without side-effects, Olestra is sure to be a hit. The age of pleasure eating – no pain, no gain, and to hell with the consequences – is upon us. Even if it could mean risking the most humiliating social gaffe of all in search of the perfect diet food.

© *SHE Magazine*
June, 1996

Food for thought

If you're busily trying to juggle work, study and family, where do you turn for help? Last week, a woman who turns to chocolate asked for advice on compulsive eating

My problem is that I am a compulsive eater. I eat in secret, whatever I can lay my hands on, preferably chocolate. I am deeply ashamed of what I do, but I seem to crave a "full" feeling at all times. In the meantime, my weight is going up and up, and I feel gross. My life is pretty stressful, juggling work, family and studying, and I am terrified of failing. I am anxious the whole time and have no confidence in my abilities. What can I do?'

Like you, I am a compulsive over-eater. These days, however, my binges are rare and I am grateful for them because they force me to look hard at myself.

Like you, I always try to do too much and be perfect, while at the same time doubting my abilities. Once I had accepted that the binges meant I was hungry not from the body, but the heart and soul, things started to change. I had lost the ability to enjoy life. I forced myself to do things just for the pleasure they gave me, without judging whether I was good at them and without other benefits being derived from doing them.

Slowly, and I mean years here, the binges got less frequent. The most difficult thing will be for you to make space in your life for pure pleasure. You may have to cut down your working hours or give up your study, or force your family to help in the home. Try anything you might enjoy – singing, writing poetry, gardening, sewing – but be careful not to judge your skills. The only measure should be enjoyment, the ability of the activity to absorb your attention and make you forget the worries of the day. It will take time to find what works for you, what will take the place of your binges.

It is up to you to love yourself enough to allow yourself just to be. Life is not about doing all the time, it is about being yourself.

Name and address withheld

It would be worthwhile seeing whether the problem is a physical one, not emotional. My daughter, while a child, was also a compulsive eater. She was always hungry and ate bread and butter at any given opportunity. She was also aggressive, hyperactive and had itchy skin.

We took her for a cytotoxic food test and I was astonished to find her compulsive eating was due to an addiction to wheat: the more she ate, the more she wanted. It was likened to a drug addiction and the symptoms can include depression, a feeling of being full and anxiety.

Within four days of cutting out the foods she was most allergic to, she was a different person. She became calm and able to sleep at night, and lost her craving for food.

Valerie Foote, Heslington, York

I am a recovering alcoholic, but I also suffer from compulsive eating, something I have not 'recovered' from. Part of the difficulty is that I have to eat something, whereas I don't have to drink alcohol.

Whenever I am emotionally unstable – which is often, as I have a stressful job and an unsatisfactory love life – I turn to food for comfort. Not lettuce and broccoli, but comfort foods – starches and sugary, sweet or creamy things. Compulsive eating is fraught with complexities: there's the food habit born of family relationships and education, and the underlying emotional problems that can range from an inability to express and understand one's anger or sadness, to issues of shame and sex. Some people are chocoholics, some have learned bad eating habits which are then compounded by associated reactions to rejection and being fat, such as self-hatred.

It is an irrational illness. You would think that someone who experiences sexual rejection, for example, would simply stop eating fattening things. But what normally happens is that, after a miserable starvation period and attempts to 'control', compulsive eaters will just go on a self-destructive binge. Such eaters use food like a drug, seeking 'instant relief' from emotional pain and emptiness.

Control is an underlying factor. Most compulsive eaters are failed

perfectionists and control freaks. It is not proven that hypnosis or behavioural therapy works, rather than just sending subliminal messages to do with control, but without helping to raise inner awareness and a sense of self-worth. A great problem is a lack of understanding in the medical and psychiatric professions.

One thing is clear: there is very little help for compulsive eaters, because to be fat denotes weakness, greed and a lack of self-respect, and is often deemed to be sexually unattractive. Make no mistake: compulsive over-eating can also be life-threatening. It can cause the slow death of the heart and lead to long-term depression and suicide.

In my experience, the best help comes from those who have suffered and can offer understanding and personal experience of recovery.

Name and address withheld

Your food problem is a mirror image of mine until five years ago. Since then my life, my sanity and my marriage have all literally been saved.

On the outside I was Mrs Superwoman, a caring wife and

I started eating three proper meals a day and nothing in between, and I lost three stone

---

mother of three, part-time worker and active on the school PTA. But my weight was escalating by the week.

Inside, my self-esteem had become so low and my eating so totally out of control that I didn't know which way to turn. My secret bingeing was making me a prisoner. I was repulsed by my own body and appearance.

I 'knew' everything there was to know about diets, but the results were only a short-lived fix and the compulsion to eat continued.

Then a recovering alcoholic friend told me about Over-eaters Anonymous. At my first 'meeting', I heard men and women of all shapes and sizes talk about compulsive eating as being a dangerous illness and addiction, akin to alcoholism.

How painful yet surprising it was to hear other people talking openly about their secret problem with food. Suddenly I realised that I wasn't alone. And what a relief to hear that Over-eaters Anonymous does not promote diets or calorie-counting, but follows a path to recovery along the same lines as Alcoholics Anonymous, using their 12-step programme but changing the words alcohol and alcoholic to food and compulsive over-eating.

That first meeting was five years ago. I started learning to appreciate myself and began to be able to put food in its rightful place. I learned to deal with my fears and insecurities and to accept that neither I nor anyone else had to be perfect. I began living in the answer, not the problem.

I started eating three proper meals a day and nothing in between, and I lost three stone. I accept that food will always be a problem for me but with Over-eaters Anonymous, I have hope. They are at PO Box 19, Stretford, Manchester M32 9EB.

Name and address withheld

Fatty issue sparks food protest

Plans by the food giant Procter & Gamble to introduce a revolutionary and controversial 'fat-free fat' into Britain will go ahead despite claims that the product has unpleasant side-effects.

Olestra has already been approved for use in snack foods by authorities in the United States, and crisps containing the product are being test-marketed among American consumers by the potato chip manufacturer Frito-Lay.

But safe food campaigners in Britain claim that the substance is 'anti-nutritional . . . and will not encourage healthier diets'. Dr Tim Lobstein, co-director of the Food Commission, said: 'There have been complaints from people trying olestra

that it 'leaks', leading to stained underwear, and that it makes the toilet oily.'

Because of its unique chemical composition, olestra, which is manufactured from sugar and vegetable oil, adds no fat or calories to food. But the US Federal Drug Administration, in backing the product earlier this year, said it may cause cramping and loose stools. It concluded that the side-effects would not normally carry medical consequences, but that labels should advise consumers to stop using olestra if necessary.

Lindsay Williams, UK public affairs manager for Procter & Gamble, confirmed that the company had applied to the Ministry

of Agriculture, Fisheries and Food for olestra to be approved in Britain. He declined to confirm that Pringles potato chips would be among the first products to contain olestra if it was sanctioned.

Mr Williams dismissed the Food Commission's fears as 'an old chestnut', insisting that the problem of 'oily leaks' may have existed early on, but had now been solved. 'What olestra does is allow people to enjoy the great taste of fat without actually having fat in their diet,' he said. Mr Williams insisted that olestra was not being sold as a slimming aid, but as a healthy alternative to fat.

The key to slimming without pain

Human tests planned after protein turns fat mice into thin ones. Roger Highfield reports

Daily injections of a protein tested successfully on overweight mice hold out hope for humans who long to shed pounds without suffering the pain of dieting or strenuous exercise.

The key to a potentially powerful method to tackle obesity, the most common nutritional disorder in the Western world, emerges in research published today in the journal *Science*. At its simplest, the protein works on mice by fooling their bodies into believing they have too much fat. This reduces appetites and increases energy consumption.

However, even if the treatment is eventually proved safe for humans, its introduction is likely to be some years away.

One third of people in Britain carry too much fat and about one in 20 of the population is obese – weighing 20 per cent or more above their maximum desirable body weight.

The protein was discovered with the help of a strain of fat mice, called obese or 'ob mice'. The protein injections cut their weight by 30 per cent after two weeks of treatment, according to scientists of the Howard Hughes Medical Institute, Rockefeller University, in New York.

'We must proceed cautiously to prove that the protein treatment is safe in animals,' said the team leader, Prof Jeffrey Friedman. 'Studies of humans cannot begin until the protein has been confirmed to be without unwanted side-effects.'

The hormone-like protein has been named leptin by Prof Friedman, from the Greek root *leptos* meaning thin.

Trials on humans are planned next year. The treatment would involve injections as the protein's molecule – like insulin's – is so large that it would be broken down and digested rather than absorbed. For this reason it is unlikely to be available in a pill form.

Explaining how leptin works, Prof Friedman likened the body's fat control mechanism to a thermostat: it senses leptin levels and adjusts fat deposits accordingly by regulating how much food is eaten and how much is turned into energy.

> **One third of people in Britain carry too much fat and about one in 20 of the population is obese**

'Each of us is set to have a different amount of body fat, which we maintain by the action of this protein and other genes,' said Prof Friedman, who collaborated with British-born Prof Stephen Burley. Injections of the protein fool the body into thinking there is too much fat, so it cuts appetite and increases consumption of energy.

The work can be traced back to 1950, when a team at the Jackson Laboratory in Bar Harbour in Maine discovered the obese (ob) mouse. Last December Prof Friedman's team reported discovering the gene, called ob, that was responsible for the mouse's great girth.

The researchers measured the amounts of leptin in the blood and found that fat mice with a defective ob gene do not make leptin. They also found leptin in the blood of six lean humans.

'The new findings indicate that when ob is defective, leptin is not made and does not transmit its signal to stop eating,' said Dr Jeffrey Halaas of Rockefeller. Consequently, mice with a faulty ob gene are overweight and have a form of diabetes.

After two weeks of treatment with leptin, the ob mice lost 30 per cent of their body weight, without side-effects and exclusively from fat loss. Treated ob mice had 9.1 grams of fat while untreated ob mice had 38.30 grams of fat. A normal, healthy adult mouse has between two and five grams of fat.

'The effect of the laboratory-derived leptin on food intake and body weight in mice is dramatic,' said Prof Burley. Leptin treatment not only reduced food consumption in the ob mice – by 60 per cent after four days – but also increased their energy output.

The researchers put a group of untreated ob mice on a low calorie diet and fed them only as much food as eaten by the treated ob mice. The result was that the food-restricted mice lost less weight than their cousins given leptin: 11 gram loss in dieting mice versus 16 gram loss in leptin mice.

Importantly, even normal mice receiving leptin lost about 12 per cent of their weight and almost all of their body fat.

Both mouse leptin and human leptin reduced weight in ob mice. 'The fact that human leptin reduces weight in the mice raises the possibility that giving leptin to people might have similar effects,' Prof Friedman said.

The scientists now want to understand how leptin transmits its weight-reducing signal. Prof Friedman notes that the hypothalamus, the part of the brain that coordinates basic body functions such as food intake, is likely to receive leptin's signal, either directly or indirectly.

Amgen, a biotechnology company based in Thousand Oaks, California, reportedly agreed to pay a £13 million advance fee to Rockefeller for rights to the gene. One third of this will go to the researchers. The amount paid could rise to £70 million if the protein lives up to expectations.

Dr Frank Collins of Amgen said human trials could begin in about a year if preliminary studies went well. The protein would be tested first on monkeys, whose conditions mimic human obesity.

The ob gene and its protein product are far from the whole story. Yesterday, scientists from Millennium Pharmaceuticals in America announced they have found the tubby gene, in studies of another overweight mouse called tubby.

'The tubby mouse very much resembles human obesity in terms of the timing of onset of the overweight condition and the distribution of fat tissue,' said Dr Jules Hirsch of Rockefeller University.

There are also other approaches: for instance, antibodies that destroy fat cells – 'biotech liposuction' – developed by Dr Chris Henshaw of the National Institute for Medical Research, with Dr David Flint of the Hannah Research Institute in Ayr.

The company, Obesys, hopes to offer this approach for trials in three years' time.

'Our technique has the ability to be used locally, in specific areas of the body,' said Dr Flint – on the buttocks, face, legs or belly without reducing fat levels elsewhere.

Britons urged to walk themselves fitter

By Liz Hunt,
Health Editor

Health ministers yesterday appealed to an increasingly slothful nation to heave itself up from the couch and indulge in a little activity.

A £9m fitness campaign launched in Docklands, east London, yesterday will urge people to walk further, use the stairs instead of lifts, and cycle rather than drive.

The Health Education Authority, which is running the three-year campaign, said the aim was to persuade people to adapt their lives to include some exertion, without pushing themselves too strenuously.

Baroness Cumberlege, junior health minister, who described herself as a keen cyclist and gardener, said: 'We do not have to be Olympic champions or pump iron to keep fit. The important thing is to do something regular if you can. Start to build up to moderate activity five times a week – you will certainly reap the benefits.'

The minister, 53, said she practised what she was preaching: 'I do cycle and I've done the London-to-Brighton bike run. I'm also a farmer's wife and so it's quite hard to avoid exercise when you live on a farm – especially when the bullocks get out.'

Research has shown significant health improvements result from building up to five 30 minute sessions of moderate physical activity a week.

Nick Cavill, HEA's physical activity manager, said: 'Five 30-minute sessions a week is a goal. Any activity is better than none, particularly if you haven't been active for some time. So build up slowly, and think of all the ways that you could be a little more active . . . It's not necessary to go jogging or run around a squash court. Brisk walking, cycling, swimming and dancing are ideal.'

The initiative follows concern that more than half the British population is overweight, and that one person in three is classed as sedentary. Between 1980 and 1992 the overweight population increased by 15 per cent to 54 per cent of men and 45 per cent of women. Other developed and emerging countries show a similar trend, and the World Health Organisation last week launched a campaign to tackle obesity.

There is growing evidence for the benefits of physical exercise which protects against heart disease, high blood pressure, cancer, osteoporosis, diabetes and arthritis. It is also a valuable aid to stress relief.

The Active For Life campaign will be promoted on television initially, and by posters in libraries, community centres and doctors' surgeries.

Why slimming ads are bad for health

From the National Food Alliance Project on Food Advertising

The UK slimming industry is estimated to have an annual turnover of approximately £1 billion. Yet the number of overweight and obese people in the UK is increasing at an alarming rate. If current trends continue, it has been estimated that 18% of men and 24% of women will be obese by 2005. At the same time there is increasing concern about the incidence of eating disorders such as anorexia and bulimia.

The dream that a physical ideal can be achieved through the latest diet fad retains its appeal despite the fact that the majority of people who embark upon diets to lose weight fail to do so in the long term. The medical and scientific consensus that has now emerged is that the way to maintain a healthy weight is to ensure that calorie intake does not exceed calorie expenditure; that is by eating a healthy balanced diet and by being physically active throughout life.

Advertising plays an important role in maintaining the myth of 'miracle' or easy weight loss and thus undermining this important health message. Slimming adverts are a special area where many of those reading adverts are likely to want to believe the claims (however outrageous) of advertisers because of the vulnerability and often desperation of those who have sought (usually unsuccessfully) to lose weight permanently.

There is growing evidence about the ill-effects on health of rapid weight loss and 'yo-yo' dieting. Safe weight loss is generally considered to be no more than 1-2lbs a week. A recently agreed EC Directive on Foods intended for Use in Energy Restricted Diets, due to be implemented in the UK in 1997, states that no advertising, labelling or presentation of a product should make any reference to the rate or amount of weight loss which may result from their use, or to a reduction in the sense of hunger or an increase in the sense of satiety. This is a welcome step and the National Food Alliance (NFA) Advertising Working Party proposes that this requirement should apply to all slimming products and services.

There is growing evidence about the ill-effects on health of rapid weight loss and 'yo-yo' dieting

Alongside growing concern about obesity, the problems of anorexia and bulimia are increasingly being recognised. A significant proportion of both teenage and pre-adolescent girls say that they are on weight reducing diets. Under-nutrition at a time of physical growth and development has been found to have detrimental effects on metabolism and may lead to retarded growth, delayed puberty and to osteoporosis later in life.

Many adult women restrict their diets beyond what is beneficial to their health. Dieting has been shown to have wide-ranging consequences for psychological function including altering the way information is processed, impairing cognitive performance and increasing preoccupation with food. Concern about food and weight can lead to eating problems and, in more severe cases, anorexia and bulimia. Research has found that fifteen year old girls who diet are eight times more likely to develop eating disorders than non-dieters. Therefore, the NFA report argues, every effort should be made to ensure that all advertisements, not just those for slimming products, do not encourage undue pre-occupation with slimness or dieting or encourage anyone, but particularly children and young adults, to lose weight unnecessarily.

While the advertising Code does preclude slimming adverts from being targetted at the under 18s, the use of ultraslim models in advertising generally is not prohibited.

What needs to be done

The NFA report argues that it is vitally important to ensure, not only that there are adequate rules, but that they are effectively enforced. It is this latter function of the Advertising Standards Authority (ASA) which the report heavily criticises.

The ASA has no legal powers, though it does investigate when complaints are made against adverts. If a complaint is upheld, the ASA's sanctions are usually limited to an admonishment published in its monthly reports and a request for advertisers to seek advice before publishing further advertisements. Few of the complaints upheld receive widespread publicity so members of the public are unlikely to be made aware.

The report proposes that the most effective way of ensuring that all advertising complies with the rules is for adverts to be pre-vetted by an independent body. In this way publishers would be instructed only to accept adverts which had prior approval.

In addition the report recommends detailed guidance notes for advertisers, their agencies and publishers which would assist those who claim they did not fully understand the rules. Unfortunately slimming advertising tends to attract a disproportionately large number of rogue advertisers, who have scant regard for advertising Codes. The report argues that prompt legal action and fines against such advertisers is the only answer. While Trading Standards Officers have the powers to take misleading advertisers to court, with the potential to impose large fines, the ASA at present can only refer persistent offenders to the Office of Fair Trading for legal action. Since 1988 only two cases have been taken up by the OFT, only one of which resulted in a court injunction and neither of which resulted in fines.

The NFA proposes that fines for Code transgressions should be levied, and that all publications that carried the advert should print equally prominent corrections.

● The above is an extract from *Adwatch*, the newsletter of the National Food Alliance Project on Food Advertising.

Television 'feeds children diet of junk food'

By Celia Hall, Medical Editor

Junk food promotions account for up to three-quarters of food advertisements screened at peak viewing times for children, a report claims today.

Children see three to four times more advertisements for drinks and fatty, sugary and salty food than adults who watch after 9.30pm, according to the National Food Alliance report, *Easy to Swallow, Hard to Stomach*.

This undermines parental authority on diet and goes against Government health recommendations, it says.

'The foods we should eat the least are the most highly advertised while the foods we should eat the most are the least advertised,' said Sue Dibb, the alliance's advertising project officer.

'This not only encourages and reinforces children's consumption of foods which do little to contribute to a healthy diet, it also undermines the efforts of parents and others to encourage healthier eating.'

Seven in 10 advertisements screened in the afternoons and on Saturday mornings were for food, compared to two in 10 in the evenings. Forty-four to 76 per cent were for soft drinks, crisps and ice creams.

Only two of the 549 advertisements monitored were for 'healthy' food, apples and pears, according to the alliance, which represents health, environmental and consumer organisations.

Researchers monitored children's television over two periods, in 1994 and in May this year. They watched programmes between 3.30pm and 5.10pm, on Saturday mornings from 6am to 1pm, *The Big Breakfast* on weekdays from 7am to 9am and adult programmes from 9.30pm to 11pm.

> **'The foods we should eat the least are the most highly advertised while the foods we should eat the most are the least advertised'**

They found that, during children's TV, confectionery and breakfast cereals, most of which were highly-sweetened, were the most intensively-advertised foods.

'Much of the remaining food was for soft drinks, fast food, savoury snacks and ice cream and lollies,' according to the alliance, which claims that current advertising codes are ineffective as they apply to individual advertisements and not to their cumulative effect.

The report says: 'The codes should prohibit advertisements from 'disparaging good nutritional practice' or from encouraging or condoning 'excessive consumption' of the kind of foods we are being encouraged to eat less frequently.'

It calls on the Government to oblige the Independent Television Commission to look at this cumulative effect when drawing up codes of practice. It wants to ban advertisements for fatty sugary foods when large numbers of children are likely to be watching television. Twice as many children aged four to nine watch children's TV as those aged 10-15.

The food advertising unit of the Advertising Association said that advertising was 'far less influential than family and peers' in framing consumer behaviour, insisting: 'Young people use advertising, not the other way around.'

Jenina Bas, its spokesman on children and food, said: 'Advertising literacy is a skill children acquire as part of growing up and parents can and do ensure they acquire this skill.'

She said that Christmas was a useful time when children 'can be taught the social and economic value judgements'.

Danger drugs freely given to all who ask

Women often unaware of potential perils as they strive for 'unnatural ideal'

By Rebecca Fowler

For thousands of slimmers it was irresistible: a pill that makes you thin. But the cost has proved higher than they imagined, with evidence that 15 deaths have been linked to the controversial drugs, and that many more users have suffered disturbing side-effects.

In recent years the pills have become an increasingly prominent part of the £1bn slimming industry in Britain. Many users experienced a dramatic weight loss in a matter of only weeks while using the drugs, which suppress the appetite or speed up the metabolism.

But the use of the pills, obtained mostly from private slimming clinics, has caused growing concern among medical experts. Among the side effects are addiction, insomnia, depression, hair-loss, restlessness, hallucinations and, at worst, death.

Despite efforts to control the spread of the drugs, handed out in liberal quantities by the clinics for between £25 and £50 for a six-week supply, their attraction has been widespread among anxious slimmers, many of whom are not even medically overweight.

The Duchess of York and Whitney Houston, the singer, have reportedly taken slimming drugs. Ms Houston was rushed to hospital with an irregular heartbeat after she attempted to shed weight quickly following the birth of her daughter in 1993.

Dr Michael Spira, adviser to Slimmers Clubs UK, is among those who do not wish to see the drugs banned, but brought under more rigid control, for use only in extreme cases of obesity. He believes the drugs should only be available on NHS prescriptions, from approved doctors and specialists in obesity.

Dr Spira stressed the best way to lose weight for most people was a healthy diet, with low fat and refined sugar contents, and plenty of exercise. He said: 'Pills should only really be prescribed for people who are extremely overweight and have tried traditional methods of dieting and have failed.'

The drugs fall into two main groups: appetite suppressants, stimulants which work like amphetamines, speeding up the metabolism and burning up more energy; and diuretics which can strip the body of water and potassium.

The most disturbing trend is the use of the drugs among women who are not medically overweight, but still wish to shed pounds. Many are competing with the waif-like figures of catwalk models like Kate Moss and Jodie Kidd, who have created an unnatural ideal.

One of the first casualties was Mavis Fryer, a former model who died three years ago, aged 52, after an addiction to slimming pills that spanned 30 years. She first started taking them when Twiggy, the first super-waif, had created the look.

Miss Fryer was forced to take more and more pills for them to take effect, but her weight still ballooned to 15 stone, and when she died she was taking 20 times the recommended dose of Duromine.

Shirley Farrell, 36, a receptionist from Dagenham, Essex, is among those who had a genuine weight problem, but experienced disturbing side-effects from slimming pills and

Slimming pills

Chemical name	Brand name	Possible side-effects	Contra-indications
Dexfenfluramine / Fenfluramine	Ponderax Adipomin Ponderal	Diarrhoea, drowsiness, dizziness, headaches, loss of libido, impotence, blood disorders, pulmonary, hypertension, schizo-phrenia-like reactions	Not to be taken if pregnant, epilectic or with a history of depression, or drug or alcohol abuse
Phentermine	Adipex Duromine Ionamin	Dry mouth, headache, rushes, dependence, insomnia, depression, psychosis, hallucination, hypertension	Not to be taken if pregnant or breast feeding, suffering from epilepsy, glaucoma, unstable personality, severe hypertension, history of drug abuse
Diethylpropion	Tenuate Dospan Apisate	As above	As above

also found the weight loss temporary. She went to a private clinic in Ilford when her weight reached 18 stone and paid £500 for a six-month course of pills.

'The doctor didn't even give me a medical check-up. He simply weighed me and dished out pills and a diet sheet,' she said. 'I still don't know what they were. It's ripping people off when they're extremely vulnerable. When you're really overweight, you're so desperate you'd try anything.'

Although Ms Farrell lost three stone, she regained the weight as soon as she stopped taking the pills, and she also suffered from depression and fatigue. Only when she left the clinic and followed a healthy eating plan, did her weight drop properly to 11st 8lb.

Fatty puffs

Despite official exhortations to eat less and exercise more, Britons get fatter and fatter. The government's annual health survey, the results of which are to be published later this month, will show that the nation's waistline continues to expand unchecked. Britons today weigh, on average, 9lbs more than Britons did in 1980.

The results will be a great disappointment to Baroness Cumberlege, the pencil-slim minister for health. Only two weeks ago she declared that good progress was being made in improving the nation's diet. 'We now have a sound basis', she claimed, 'to help us achieve the "Health of the Nation" targets.' In fact, health officials accept that there is not the slenderest hope of meeting the target set in the strategy document published in 1992 – which was to trim the nation's waistline back to what it was in 1980.

In the past 15 years, the proportion of people in England and Wales who are overweight has risen by more than one-sixth, to 54% of men and 45% of women. The number of those who are dangerously fat has doubled: 13% of men and 16% of women are now regarded as clinically obese. People who are obese are six times more likely to suffer from high blood pressure, diabetes, high cholesterol and heart disease, according to estimates by the World Health Organisation.

Ministers say they are concerned about the swelling of the nation, but they are also rightly nervous about being accused of running a nanny-state so bossy that even nannies would disapprove. They are no less anxious, one suspects, to avoid offending the manufacturers of processed food. A report on obesity by the Nutrition Task Force (a committee set up by the government as part of its new health strategy) was published last November. But that was only after *The Economist* asked the Department of Health why it had been suppressed.

In the past 15 years, the proportion of people in England and Wales who are overweight has risen by more than one-sixth

---

The Nutrition Task Force has now been wound up. It is true that its job was to find facts and inform the public, and no more than that. But the real reason for its demise, according to the scientists who served on the task force, was the refusal of food manufacturers to co-operate. It asked 16 trade associations representing parts of the food industry to help identify ways of reducing the fat in their products. One replied with the information.

Britain's failure to reduce fat in food contrasts with the record of some other countries. Over the past 15 years, the inhabitants of Norway and Finland have reduced the proportion of food energy they derive from fat from 42% to 34%. One result has been a marked drop in levels of blood-cholesterol. The number of Norwegian men dying from heart disease has fallen by 40% in just over a decade. Britain continues to have one of the highest rates of deaths due to heart disease in Western Europe.

Weight on their minds

11-year-old boys who live in fear of being fatties

A growing number of boys aged only 11 are risking their health because they fear they are overweight, experts warned yesterday.

While young girls try to look like skinny supermodels, the boys are under increasing pressure to conform to ideal slim images of pop bands such as Take That.

Half of girls and a third of boys aged 11 and 12 have anxieties about the shape and weight of their bodies, a Health Education Authority Survey revealed.

Eleven per cent of the boys said they were unhappy with their shape, weight and height.

One-fifth were dissatisfied with certain aspects of their body such as their stomach or chest.

They said they lacked self-confidence and have low self-esteem because they did not possess the perfect physique.

Yet nutrition experts say only about five per cent are overweight.

One in ten of Britain's 70,000 anorexia sufferers are male and the proportion is increasing.

'Peer pressure and fashion images seem to be responsible for these problems of poor body image,' said the HEA's Lucy Thorne.

'Boys are perhaps motivated by the new "boy bands". There are many more men's fashion magazines on the market and they want to be as glamorous as their sporting heroes.'

Parents had to realise that their own dietary preoccupations could affect their children, she added.

'What is important is that parents do not belittle their children's fears,' she said.

Dr Robert Peveler, senior lecturer in psychiatry at Southampton University, said the new trend was 'very worrying'.

He added: 'Young people used to have a much healthier set of concerns but the ideal images are much more extreme now.'

The HEA surveyed 287 boys and 248 girls aged 11 and 12 in London schools.

One girl told researchers: 'I used to be so skinny. I have got photos of me when I was really skinny and dressed up and now it really makes me sick to see that I have put on so much weight.' The survey also showed that parents need help in discussing sensitive issues such as weight, sex and depression with their children.

Kathy Elliott, director of Family and Child Health at the HEA, said: 'Parents want reassurance about what is "normal" behaviour, what should worry them and how to respond to sensitive questions.'

The HEA recommends that parents should be offered guidance at five key stages – antenatal, post-natal, for the pre-school child, for five to eleven year-olds and for teenagers.

The report also found that mothers tend to be the guardians of their families' health but need more support to cope with their own health fears. Fathers are likely to play only a peripheral role in shaping the family's health.

And men and boys both need greater health awareness in areas of stress, sex education, relationships and reproductive health.

The HEA research was presented to a special conference on health promotion and the family in London yesterday.

Taunts drove son to despair

Stuart Miller almost killed himself running up and down the stairs hundreds of times a day as he frantically tried to lose weight.

The 11-year-old was convinced that all problems the he had at school would vanish if only he were slim. But one day he collapsed, and was taken to hospital, where he was put on drips and heart monitors as he clung to life. He weighed less than five stone.

Slimming down did not end Stuart's nightmare at school, said his mother Gillian.

The bullies who had put vinegar on his food, pushed him into bins and locked him in cupboards still taunted him.

'They said, "Keep away from us Miller, you've got Aids" and laughed at him for being thin,' said Mrs Miller at the family home in Longridge, near Preston. 'His self-esteem and confidence was so low it was just terrible.'

Last month, Stuart's family told *the Daily Mail* of the pressures that drove the youngster, now 15, to anorexia.

At the time he was still in Rhodes Farm Clinic, North London, trying to overcome his illness. Today he is living at home and has been a college student for four weeks.

'He is coping, but it's difficult and we're taking things a step at a time,' said Mrs Miller.

'He finds college difficult – there is so much sitting around so he cannot exercise, and he finds lunchtime absolutely terrifying because he eats unsupervised. But he's doing OK.'

Stuart left the clinic when he reached his target weight of 8st 7lb and has to eat 2,250 calories a day to maintain that level.

However, Mrs Miller says the problems now are nothing compared to those when Stuart was in the throes of anorexia.

'I wanted to look like a model'

As the report points out, young girls dream of being like skinny supermodels.

Cara Thorneycroft, an intelligent 12-year-old, wanted to be like the pictures she saw in fashion magazines.

'I saw thin models and I wanted to look like that,' she said. 'In three months I was down to 4st 4lb and I went into hospital to be fed by a tube.'

Cara, from Kibworth, Leicestershire, is anorexic. She is convinced she is fat.

And she is terrified about how she will look when she reaches her target weight of 7st 4lbs, set for her by Rhodes Farm Clinic, run in the family home of Dr Dee Dawson.

'I'm here for the second time,' says Cara, who first started dieting when she was ten.

'I've been here eight weeks now and I'm worried because they put my target weight up since last time and I know I must reach it.

'I started dieting after I was weighed at school and I was heavier than everyone else because I was taller. Girls started laughing at me and calling me fat. I was upset and I started dieting and exercising. Eventually I stopped eating altogether.'

She entered the clinic and after 16 weeks reached her target weight of just under 7st and returned to school. But she was teased again.

'I haven't been to school since last November,' said Cara. 'By Christmas I couldn't eat. I didn't want to go back to the clinic but I had to or I was going to be put into care.'

© *The Daily Mail*
March, 1996

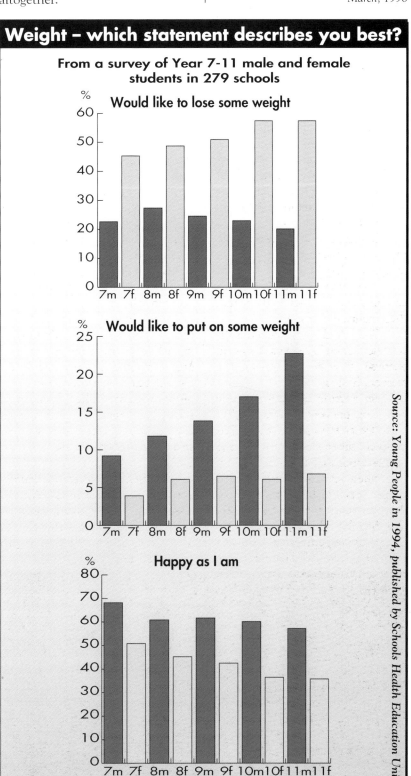

Weight – which statement describes you best?

From a survey of Year 7-11 male and female students in 279 schools

Source: Young People in 1994, published by Schools Health Education Unit
Source: Young People in 1994, published by Schools Health Education Unit

Understanding eating distress

Information from MIND

We all need food to live; it is an essential part of our daily lives, regulated by appetite and the clock. In times of stress however, our 'normal' eating patterns often change. We may develop cravings for certain foods, lose our appetite or eat more for comfort. This is a natural response experienced by many people, particularly women, but it usually resolves once the problem is overcome.

However for some people life may become centred around food. Whether denying it to themselves, eating, or thinking about it, food becomes like an addiction and starts dominating their whole existence. Yet we all have to eat or we die.

As a person who has had direct personal experience of the vicious cycle of denial/abuse that is a characteristic of eating distress, I also know that during those nightmarish years, denying myself was the only thing that kept me alive.

Eating distress is viewed on the one hand as a serious psychological problem needing psychiatric treatment, whilst on the other, the media simply define it as 'slimmers disease'. The material in this article offers alternative approaches to this complex subject – exploring the causes as well as the effects.

There are no easy recipes for curing eating distress – everyone's experience is individual, but we hope that through reading this you will gain a deeper understanding of its powerful statement, so that both those affected as well as close friends and relatives feel there is a way out.

What is it?

It is an expression of deep emotional conflict which results in the individual experiencing a distressed relationship with food. Eating itself may provoke feelings of fear, anxiety, guilt and self-hatred. The individual may feel unable to eat with others, and become socially isolated. Depression, disordered sleep patterns, restlessness and disturbance of bodily functions are some of the effects. It is important to remember that these problems are symptoms – the effects of underlying distress which are often deeply linked to the person's need to be valued, respected and acknowledged as an individual. They are not the cause itself.

'My whole life became one governed by fear. I felt trapped, controlled . . . so I sought to control the one area of my life I could . . . that of food – yet soon that too consumed me . . .'
Eating Distress: Perspectives from Personal Experience

'Compulsive eating', 'bulimia' and 'anorexia' are the more common medical 'labels' given to the varying symptoms of eating distress. However in practice there is no clear boundary between them, as all, in their own ways, severely damage the individual.

Compulsive eating

Such individuals can be, but are not necessarily, overweight. It is neither greed nor hunger that drives them to eat constantly. They may feel unable either to regulate or make decisions regarding their dietary intake. They feel the powerless victims of food and yet are constantly trying to gain control.

Compulsive eating usually occurs when the individual is feeling distressed, anxious or angry. At these times any type of food and any amount may be consumed regardless of appetite, taste or time of day. A specific food can act as a 'trigger' – chocolate or high sugar items – but this is not always the case; the urgency is the desperate need to get something into the mouth.

'Eating was comforting, pleasurable, an attempt to make up for everything I didn't have . . . The worse things became for me . . . the more I ate . . .'
Eating Distress: Perspectives from Personal Experience

Compulsive eating may be accompanied by self-induced vomiting. In between the more difficult times – before the next uncontrollable impulse occurs – are often periods of strict dieting and rigid food control.

Bulimia

Unlike anorexia, the distress experienced by an individual suffering with bulimia may go unnoticed. The person may be any weight or size and not look ill. They may appear to be in control of their external lives, coping fairly successfully on a day to day basis. Yet they are tormented by an unpredictable cycle of chaotic eating. This may range from periods of total starvation to eating thousands of calories at one time – generally alone – and is accompanied by self-induced vomiting. Abuse of laxatives and diuretics (drugs which induce greater bowel movements and urination) are other methods of self-harm resorted to in desperate attempts to 'gain control'. All these forms of abuse can occur regardless of how much actual food is consumed and the consequences – both physical and mental – can be severe.

Anorexia

This does not necessarily imply a 'loss of appetite' as is often assumed. Anorexia is more about denial. The individual may experience severe hunger and long to allow themselves to eat. But denying themselves the right to eat may be the only means available to them of controlling their lives. 'Giving in' is seen as reinforcing all the conflicts they are trying so hard to survive, even if survival paradoxically may result in death.

Food and fluid intake is restricted to low calorie items, and often carefully measured. Eating with others may become a nightmare as others may attempt to 'force-feed', and a ritual of secret and isolated eating often occurs. The individual may also embark upon vigorous exercise regimes and weigh themselves several times a day. Life becomes centred around food, weight and body size.

Although perceptions of body size and self become distorted to a degree in all forms of eating distress, for a person experiencing anorexia, these feelings may be magnified out of all proportion – however thin, they still see themselves as fat.

There may be times however when deep bodily instincts for food become so overwhelming that huge and frightening eating binges result, which only perpetuate the individual's distress. Self-induced vomiting, laxative and sometimes diuretic abuse may be further measures used in order to 'purge the body of poison' however little has been eaten.

Medical consequences

These can apply to the three 'labelled' symptom pictures described above and may include:
- tooth decay and gastric erosion (especially if there is vomiting);
- blood disturbances and mineral imbalances in the body;
- bodily hair growth;
- disturbed menstrual functioning;
- low blood sugar;
- heart, kidney and intestinal damage;
- bowel damage;
- severe fluctuations in body temperature;
- a variety of mental symptoms: anxiety and panic attacks, hallucinations, fainting and dizziness, insomnia and depression.

There is also a greater incidence of self-mutilation, suicide attempts and other forms of self-harm.

Who does it affect?

A large majority of the population, especially women, at some point in their lives experience a certain degree of dissatisfaction with their body weight and size. Various dietary regimes and exercise programmes may be tried, and food itself may become categorised into 'good' and 'bad' – the bad being food with greater calorific value. These episodes usually present no particular difficulties and the individual's 'normal' eating habits are generally restored with no lasting effects.

However, eating distress is affecting more and more people (an estimated 60,000 to 200,000 in the UK alone). Though primarily affecting women in their teens and early twenties, in recent years more men and even children younger than ten have been reported as suffering. Recent research results show that one in three nine-year-old girls are worried about their weight, and that many are already dieting.

What causes it?

A number of theories have been put forward. These have included difficulties within the family, relationship with mother, sexuality and gender issues, emotional/physical abuse, fear of growing up, reaction to stressful life events etc. Depending upon the individual, some of these issues may play a part along the road to distressed eating, but they are not the whole story. For this, we need to consider the wider context.

Social/political

'Sexism transcends . . . class, race and religion. It is a culture in itself.'
Eating Distress: Perspectives from Personal Experience

'Until now eating disorders have been exclusive to a Western culture obsessed with slender figures but now they are believed to symbolise revolt among young Asian girls trying to straddle two cultures.' Guardian 5.3.91
'Many men won't speak out about how rigid definitions of sexuality stop them from fulfilling themselves.'
Eating Distress: Perspectives from Personal Experience

Gender oppression can affect both men and women. We are expected to conform to stereotyped roles regardless of what we feel. Women, for instance, are supposed to be both universal care-giver and ideal sex symbol – to be both mother and lover – within a society largely dominated by masculine values. The work of the feminist movement exposes these conflicts and continues to present a different role of women in an attempt to find ways of redressing the balance. But for many women, and to a lesser extent men, the struggle between self and societal expectations still creates enormous difficulties and suffering.

To many individuals such conflict becomes internalised, the taking in or denial of food becoming its outward expression.

Media input

We are continually given messages through the media as to how we 'should' look, eat, dress and what we 'should' buy. Food and exercise advertisements often portray sylph-like models who use their sexuality to lure people into consuming. The message is of course that 'ideal' looks and physical size equal success and therefore demand. In addition we are presented with conflicting ideas about what is a 'normal' diet, and what foods are 'healthy'.

It can thus be extremely hard to contend with a less than perfect body in a world which puts so much value upon the 'ideal', and can therefore be severely disempowering.

Family input

If feelings and conflicts are repressed within the family, it may well be that early emotional needs were ignored. Parents may want to do the best for their children, but in fact can become overprotective and dominating. The growing child's only way to be appreciated then is through living up to parental expectations. They may not feel they are a person in their own right, nor receive acknowledgement of their individuality. Abuse, be it physical, emotional or sexual, may also be a major factor within family dynamics.

Such patterns transcend class and culture and controlling food intake may be the only way the individual can assert control over their life.

Individual

Generally those experiencing eating distress are high achievers and perfectionists. Yet they may have very low self-esteem and self-worth. Often sensitive and potentially very creative, they may experience great levels of anxiety but feel emotionally repressed.

The triggering event may be a particularly stressful situation, family or relationship crisis, adolescent conflicts, exams, leaving home – external pressures which may make them feel so powerless that they attempt to silence their emotional needs through their relationship with food.   © MIND, 1995

Did you know . . .?

Information from the Eating Disorders Association

– Eating disorders have one of the highest mortality rates of all psychiatric illnesses, over 10% of sufferers dying either from the effects of starvation or by committing suicide

– Research has shown that about 2% of women suffer from anorexia or bulimia but it is thought that the true figure is much higher than this

– There are at least 60,000 people known to be suffering from anorexia and bulimia at any one time; the figure is probably nearer 150,000 to 200,000

– Approximately 10% of sufferers are men

– Only about 50% of those diagnosed as having an eating disorder have recovered after 5 years

– Specialist treatment centres throughout UK can only treat a total of about 1,500 patients each year

– While anorexia and bulimia usually originate during adolescence, the symptoms can appear in women (and men) of all ages

– Research has shown that there is a genetic predisposition to anorexia; eating problems often 'run in families'

– Anorexia and bulimia are very secretive illnesses.

– Even when anorexia becomes apparent to everyone around, the sufferer may continue to deny it

– Many women with bulimia lead lives which in all outward appearances are very successful; they have high powered jobs, including some in the medical professions, and a hectic social schedule; their bulimia nightmare is kept hidden and secret

– It has been found that about one third of anorexics and bulimics who seek therapy have been sexually abused

– Anorexics and bulimics have very low self-esteem and little confidence

– People with eating disorders have a distorted body image – they are convinced that they are fat even when it is apparent to everyone around them that they are dangerously thin

– Eating disorders lead to a lifestyle which completely dominates the sufferer's every waking hour

– Eating disorders can have a devastating effect on family life.

● The above is an extract from a basic fact sheet published by the Eating Disorders Association. See page 39 for address details.

© Eating Disorders Association

'A New Year diet triggered my anorexia'

It started as a post-Christmas diet. Lucy never dreamed it would turn into an obsession that could ruin her life.

My boyfriend Dave and I had been seeing each other for a year. We'd got together after he split from his girlfriend, Bianca.

The trouble was, Dave shared a flat with Bianca's brother, Mike. The first time I went round there, she'd turned up 'to see Mike'. She was stunning, a tall blonde waif. 'Hi, Dave,' she smiled, ruffling his hair. I felt sick.

I didn't go to the flat again but I had to pass it every day on the way to work. Bianca's car was outside at least once a week. I trusted Dave but I didn't trust her. 'You've got nothing to worry about,' Dave reassured me. 'Maybe she does come round, but it's over. She knows that.'

That Christmas, we rented a cottage. We holed up with a crate of wine and piles of food. It was the longest time we'd spent together and we got on brilliantly.

I'd always been thin. I'm five foot six and my normal weight was eight stone. But like lots of people at Christmas, I'd put on a few pounds – enough to make my trousers and skirts uncomfortably tight. So I went on a diet. Dave told me not to be silly, but I was determined.

Back at work, I had a bowl of cornflakes for breakfast, a cottage cheese sandwich for lunch, and a diet ready meal in the evening. In restaurants I'd order a salad and a diet Coke, and tell people I'd given up drinking because I was having tests for my eczema. Within a month I was back down to eight stone.

It wasn't just the weight loss I liked, it was the feeling of being in control. I spent most of my time working out how many calories I'd eaten. Thinking about food meant I didn't have to worry about Bianca.

I decided my diet wasn't strict enough. To know exactly how many calories I'd had, I'd have to plan everything. I was starving all the time, so I kept drinking Diet Coke, smoking and thinking about my next meal.

My weight dropped to seven stone and my periods stopped. Dave commented on how thin I was but I still felt fat. 'He won't love me if I'm fat,' I told myself. 'Life will be better when I lose another half-stone.'

I skipped breakfast and cut down to 800 calories a day. I couldn't bear eating anything that wasn't in my diet. When the girls at work went for a pizza, I made excuses.

Outwardly, I came across as cool and controlled. Inside I was screaming. I spent every moment thinking about food, but looked at

fat people and thought I was better than them for controlling myself. It never occurred to me they might be happier.

My weight reached six-and-a-half stone. I'd have a black coffee for breakfast, six cans of Diet Coke and an apple during the day, and a 300-calorie ready meal and a diet yoghurt for dinner. I was starving all the time, which made me irritable.

Dave noticed the change. 'You're not yourself,' he said. 'You seem preoccupied all the time.' But he didn't matter. All that mattered was not putting on weight.

My weight loss began to slow down. My body was adjusting to the new diet. I had no energy and a permanent cold. I didn't have the willpower to eat any less so I took laxatives each night and dropped down to six stone. When I brushed my hair, it fell out. My skin looked awful and my nails cracked. But all I could see were bits of fat. I hid under baggy clothes but loved it when people said, 'You're so thin.' It made the hard work worthwhile.

Somewhere inside there was still the real me. One morning I woke up and knew it had to stop. I was lucky. My GP was sympathetic and she told me I had anorexia nervosa. I'd read about anorexics but thought they lost their appetite. 'But I'm not thin enough yet,' I told her.

The doctor sighed. 'You weigh six stone. Lose any more weight and you'll need hospitalisation.' She put me on anti-depressants which helped me to think rationally. And I went to a local self-help group. Meeting those women was a turning point. I learned that anorexia is one way of coping with life. Many of us had come from families where we were taught to suppress our feelings. While some people turn to drink or drugs, we'd tried to control it by not eating.

Recovering was a long haul. My weight stabilised at six-and-a-half stone as I learned to eat more and stop counting the calories. Slowly the good days outweighed the bad. I was frightened about what would happen as my weight rose but after six months, I'd stabilised at eight stone again. I didn't get fat.

Admitting it to Dave was the hardest thing of all. But he was fantastic. He didn't make a big fuss over food, and realised Bianca had made matters worse and asked Mike to find another flat. A year later, I moved in with Dave. You're never cured of anorexia.

When I get stressed, the first thing I do is cut down on eating, like an automatic reflex. But I understand enough about it to be able to stop myself and try to talk things through. It takes will-power to become an anorexic – and twice as much to beat it.

Where to get help
● Call the Eating Disorders Association on 01603 621414.
● Refer yourself to a psychologist. Find the Directory of Chartered Psychologists in your local library.
● Your GP should be able to help, but don't be put off if yours is one of the few who have little understanding of anorexia. Make an appointment with a different doctor but get help now. One in five anorexics die from starvation or suicide. It can cause heart attacks and fits, plus leave you sterile. *©More!*
January, 1996

Helping a friend or relative

People often think that eating disorders are just about food and weight. But they are not. They are about feelings as well.

What can you do if you think your friend or relative has an eating disorder?
You can really help by just being her friend, even when you feel your friendship is being rejected.

What can I do to help my friend?
Give time – and listen. Your friend may just need you to be there when things are hard to cope with. Listen to what she is saying. Try not to give advice, but encourage her to seek help. You should not take responsibility for her illness.

What if she doesn't accept there's a problem?
You may need to accept that your friend is not ready to tackle her eating disorder. But let her know how you are feeling. Tell her that she can come back to you later. Get some information about eating problems so you can help when your friend is ready to accept that there is a problem.

Should I change my eating habits to fit in with my friend?
No! Don't change your own eating habits. Unless your friend sees a 'normal' amount of food, she could

Eating Disorders Association

get more and more out of touch with normality. Don't let your friend make you feel guilty about eating a healthy, balanced diet. Try not to talk about food or calories.

Should I encourage my friend to eat?
No. Everyone needs to decide for themselves what to eat. Your friend is responsible for her own needs.

Why doesn't she join in like she used to?
If your friend has an eating disorder she may find it increasingly hard to join in with social events. She may want to spend more time on her own, and may become more withdrawn and isolated. Tell her why you like her and that you value her friendship. Try to include her in activities. Even if she does not join in, she will still like to be asked. It will make her feel valued as a person, and help with her self-esteem.

Should I tell her parents?
If you find it too difficult to keep it secret, or feel concerned about your

friend's safety, then tell an adult you trust. Tell your friend's parents if you really feel they should know. But let your friend know first that you are going to tell someone. You may have to face the fact that she may not like what you have done, even if you did it for the best, but in time she will probably appreciate your decision.

Will it help if I cover up for my friend?
The best way to help is to let your friend take responsibility for her own behaviour. The problem may go on longer if you cover it up. It would be helpful, though, to suggest that your friend gets professional help. She could discuss this with the Eating Disorders Association Youth Helpline, or arrange to see her doctor.
It is very important to remember that only your friend can take the responsibility for getting better. You can't do it for her. She will have to find new ways of coping. She needs to find different ways of showing her feelings, rather than by controlling what she eats. Only then will she be able to accept that eating is a necessary part of living.

● The above is an extract from *Helping a friend or relative*, published by the Eating Disorders Association. See page 39 for address details.
© Eating Disorders Association

Breaking the chains of eating disorders

Anorexia and bulimia nervosa used to be associated exclusively with overambitious slimmers. But the causes of these distressing and often secret conditions are rarely about food alone – and have as much to do with the mind as with the body. We tell the story of how two women regained control of their lives

By Marie Farquharson

In May 1995, when she was booked into St Andrews Hospital in her late thirties, Shirley Davis weighed four stone ten pounds. She was scared that she was going to die. During her five-week stay in hospital the very thought of food made her anxious and her stomach churn. Because she wasn't drinking properly, she had to be rehydrated intravenously. The invasive treatment wasn't helping, so Shirley discharged herself and went back home to the Isle of Man.

Shirley is anorexic. According to the European Anorexia Fund, one in 20 people in the UK have the same disease. But the real figure is probably higher, as many women, and increasingly men, will deny that they have a problem.

If you believe the newspapers, the blame for all this lies with supermodels Kate, Claudia and their super-thin cronies. But Shirley has had anorexia for 26 years – her problems began long before the term 'supermodel' existed. So, if the catwalk isn't to blame, why are women reducing themselves to the point of starvation by refusing to eat? Why are they shoving their fingers down their throats or swallowing handfuls of laxatives after bouts of uncontrolled eating? And what can be done to help them?

What causes eating disorders?

It's assumed that eating disorders are simply about food. But food is precisely what they are not about. According to the Eating Disorders Association, 'eating disorders are the outward expression of deep psychological and emotional turmoil.' Someone with an eating disorder has simply picked on food as a way of expressing her difficulties.

Shirley's problems began on a family holiday when she was just 13. Her sister Sue was having a wonderful time with girlfriends and boyfriends, while Shirley, two years her junior, was feeling miserable and excluded. The holiday was a terrible disappointment for her. She felt that her parents paid attention to her sister, but didn't notice her or care about her feelings. From that point on she decided to punish her father by not having afternoon tea. Then she began to cut out snacks, and gradually started reducing what she was eating at meal times. 'This was not a conscious attempt to lose weight,' explains Shirley. 'I was so unhappy with myself, I felt that I didn't deserve food because I wasn't loved. And it wasn't until I started losing weight that anybody showed any concern.'

The link between food and control

Shirley's experience of feeling unloved and unappreciated is just one way into anorexia. Eating disorders have been blamed on many things: poor nutrition, family

According to the European Anorexia Fund, one in 20 people in the UK have anorexia. But the real figure is probably higher

function, and the notion that women are afraid to be fat. But for Glenn Waller, senior lecturer in clinical psychology at University College London, the best explanation for anorexia is that the desire to lose weight is partly socially governed and partly governed by an individual's need to gain control over some aspect of her life. 'You'll commonly see a woman who is quite perfectionist, but dissatisfied,' says Waller. 'She will attempt to assert control over her life, and stumble across controlling her food intake as a way of doing this. She finds that she is quite good at dieting, and it goes on from there.'

For Glenn Waller, the causes of bulimia nervosa are quite different to those of anorexia, and are often associated with an inescapable trauma such as sexual or physical abuse. If a person can't get away physically from the cause of her distress, she'll look for mental ways. Bulimia, he explains, is a way of blocking out the trauma. Some people do it by getting drunk, others use drugs or cut themselves. For a bulimic, bingeing and vomiting provide the brief release she needs. While she's bingeing she's not aware of what's going on around or inside her. Focusing on food means she can't focus on what she's feeling or thinking.

The nutritional angle

For nutritionist Anthony Haines, eating disorders have both a psychological and a physiological element. He says that research suggests nutritional imbalances are to blame for at least 50 per cent of all schizophrenia and 85 per cent of all crime. This, he feels, makes compelling evidence for the part bad nutrition plays in eating disorders. Whether the eating disorder or the deficiency comes first is unclear, but he suspects that the two are closely linked from an early age.

A lack of the minerals zinc and magnesium is a particular indicator of an eating disorder. Though the cause is never exclusively physiological, the chances are that if you have a zinc deficiency, your risk of becoming anorexic increases. Zinc is involved in the sense of taste and in brain function. 'I've had tremendous results with giving zinc,' says Haines. 'If you don't taste food, it becomes joyless. And if you lack zinc you'll have no sense of taste. Zinc is also needed to make stomach acids, which we need to digest proteins. Without stomach acids you can't digest proteins. Without proteins you can't make enzymes. Without enzymes you can't digest food; if you can't digest food your body can't extract the nutrients to make more enzymes – and so it goes on in a vicious circle. Every anorexic or bulimic I've tested has been zinc deficient.' Haines believes that correcting a client's biochemical imbalance is the first step on the road to recovery.

Hilda Deas, a practitioner of traditional Chinese medicine (TCM) for some 20 years, finds that the business of eating or not eating masks deep problems. 'I have come across a host of causes,' she says, 'from sexual abuse, to studying the wrong subject at college, to unhappiness in a relationship. Anyone with an eating disorder is really saying, "Help me".'

In traditional Chinese medicine, bulimia is seen as a tendency to have heat in the stomach. When there is a lot of heat in the stomach, there is a tendency to overeat, because food and drink will cool the stomach temporarily. And this, says Hilda, can be helped with Chinese herbs and acupuncture. She also

believes that eating disorders can be exacerbated if a person's ability to control her blood sugar levels is poor. Such a person will often binge because she has a craving for sugar which, when satisfied, gives a brief, addictive high. But as soon as the craving is satisfied, the blood sugar levels slump again, creating the need for still more sugar.

What both the following stories have in common is that they show alternative therapies giving women control over their bodies and their lives where conventional methods had failed. In Shirley's case, neurolinguistic programming (NLP) proved successful; in the case of Jennifer (not her real name), TCM was the key. . .

Neurolinguistic programming

At 14, Shirley got her first taste of in-patient behavioural treatment. 'Every evening I had a tube shoved up my nose and down the back of my throat, which made me gag. Two great big bottles of liquid food were dripped in over night. In the morning, when the tube was taken out, it felt like my insides were coming out too.'

Shirley's health improved temporarily but at 16, feeling ugly

and unloved, she was diagnosed officially as anorexic and admitted to an adolescent psychiatric unit in Sussex. She stayed for two years. For the next few years her weight stayed low but stable, and when she qualified as an accountant she felt strong enough to apply for a job in Bermuda. There she met her fiancé Martin, but they split up when he met somebody else. After that Shirley went back to hospital another 14 times, and at 35 she was sent to a leading expert in food disorder, but couldn't face the in-patient treatment he recom-mended. Dosed with anti-depressants, appetite-stimulants and tablets to relieve nausea, she happened to read an article by Dennis Kent in her local paper.

Dennis uses NLP techniques to treat his clients. NLP draws on a variety of disciplines: Gestalt, Ericksonian hypnosis, and person-centred work are used to approach the way people behave and access emotional states in order to change them. Shirley had her first appointment in 1995.

When talking to a client Dennis will compare her eating disorder to a tree that has fallen across the highway of her life, and is blocking her progress. While conventional psychotherapy will try to find out why the tree fell in her path, his job is to get her over the tree or take her around it. 'By focusing on the way forward rather than on the manifestation of the disorder,' says Dennis, 'my client feels empowered to take control of her problem, without discussing topics she finds upsetting.'

One of the first things he asks is how she instructs herself not to eat or drink. Usually there is a kind of 'inner conversation' with a 'voice' urging her not to drink or eat. Dennis looks at the character of the voice in the dialogue: is it sharp or harmonious? Soft? Repetitive? Urgent? Then he asks his client to imagine the voice differently – speeded up, slowed down, or very loud. By changing the code in this way, the physiological and psychological response must change as well. 'It's like changing software in a computer,' says Dennis. 'So when the internal dialogue starts next time, my client can focus on what the voice sounds like, and change it. At first it takes effort to do this consciously, so I do it with her. Eventually she can do it subconsciously.'

Dennis told Shirley, who had been on anti-depressants for years, that she would begin to feel better after a few sessions. It was hard for her to believe. 'I have a big block with drinking. I don't drink enough fluid, which is more life-threatening, so we started there. At first my drinking behaviour didn't change, but Dennis said what mattered at that point was the internal messages I was giving myself about drinking.

'I wasn't starting to drink more: but I was buying myself fruit juice and thinking of what I'd like to drink, which I wouldn't have done before. Then after one session I felt quite thirsty. Usually I would lie down, go to sleep and forget about it. But I went to the fridge, and drank some of the fruit juice that I'd bought. I knew I'd never have to go without it again. It was wonderful – like lying in the sunshine. I felt that I'd been denying myself the sunshine for years, and now I just wanted to lie and bask in it.

'We've started working on my eating, and it's been hard, but it's wonderful – it seems to be working!'

Traditional Chinese medicine

Jennifer, now 30, was 5ft 11 and 12 stone, only one stone over her ideal weight, at the beginning of 1985. 'I would have been seen by others as an intelligent, bubbly and caring person. And I was. My 21st birthday party was perfect, it was the party of 1985. There I was – big, happy and surrounded by 200 people whom I loved and who loved me.'

Jennifer's bubble burst when she received a letter from a close friend of the family who told her that her increasing weight was making her mum and dad miserable. And Jennifer could make them so happy,

she read on, if she did something about it. Later she learned from her parents that this was all entirely untrue.

But in February 1985 she enrolled at Weight Watchers, determined to lose weight, and did so very effectively. But she did not follow the recommended diet at all. At the weekly meetings she was applauded by everyone else: she was the centre of attention, the achiever, just what she needed as the youngest in a family of four beautiful and successful siblings.

'Bulimia had drained me totally and left me feeling weak and dead inside, with no self-confidence'

Jennifer was so proud of her weight loss that it became an obsession. She starved all day and ate huge helpings of veg at night. She soon became bulimic – bingeing, vomiting and using laxatives. Only four months later, weighing seven-and-a-half stone, Jennifer was admitted to hospital. 'There were daily searches for laxatives under my mattress. I was taken to the loo and watched on every occasion. My basin had no plumbing attached. I was banished to the staff kitchen an hour before meals and made to stay there for an hour after, and they just pumped me full of food. I had six meals a day. At one stage I was on a drip. I left looking pregnant. It was a nightmare.'

Jennifer was granted leave to go on holiday with her mum and sister, on condition that if she didn't gain weight she'd have to return to hospital. 'Food and weight were taking over my entire existence. I knew this so well, but couldn't break the spell.'

'We've started working on my eating, and it's been hard, but it's wonderful – it seems to be working!'

Three days before Jennifer was due back at hospital she got a call from a friend who'd been cured of a drink problem by Hilda Deas. 'She'd heard of my situation and was ringing to recommend her. Both Mum and I decided we had nothing to lose.'

Hilda Deas specialises in traditional Chinese medicine. She looks at the person as a whole being, and uses acupuncture, Chinese herbs, nutrition and mild counselling to help patients regain health. She also seeks to enhance the patient's own part in the management of her health, discouraging her from seeing any improvement as the result of some outside agent.

Hilda first establishes where the problem comes from and what food means to her client. One principle of Chinese medicine is the law of the five elements. Each element corresponds to an energy channel, an organ of the body and an aspect of our spiritual makeup. The fire element, for example, controls the heart and small intestine, and emotions such as love and affection. A person who's refusing to eat for lack of love can be helped by a TCM practitioner working on the appropriate area.

Jennifer saw Hilda twice a week, but even after one session she felt so much better. 'I found Hilda's approach far more sympathetic than the hospital, where they stuffed me with milkshakes, chips and ice cream. Above all, Hilda was always at the end of the phone; this was vital at the time, as I'd scared all my friends away.

'Bulimia had drained me totally and left me feeling weak and dead inside, with no self-confidence. My clothes were falling off me, but I still thought of myself as fat.

'In August 1986 I cut my visits to Hilda to once a week. Very slowly I was beginning to have hope that I could live a normal life. Nine years on, I feel confident, proud and happy. I'm still underweight, and am constantly told so. I don't think you ever totally recover, but I feel lucky to be where I am now. I have a wonderful husband and two beautiful children. Who could want more?'

© Here's Health
January, 1996

Is the Kate Moss look really 500 years old?

A top nutritionist explodes the feminist myth about slim women . . .

Anorexic models teeter down the catwalk about to black out from malnutrition. Clothes are designed to look good only on size 8 and below. Perfectly well-shaped adolescents agonise about their weight.

Every woman in the country thinks she is too large round the waist. Thin is beautiful. But has it always been so? Have women always wanted to be thin?

Feminists blame it all on men. Women torture their bodies to near-starvation just, they say, because men want their women to be thin and torment them with images that rub it in.

And feminists point to a Golden Age when women were happy to be large, and men liked a well-built spouse with flesh to get hold of. And, as evidence, they point to all the pictures that men have made of women from the dawn of civilisation until halfway through this century.

The women in them were big. Plump. Rounded at the very least. Not to mince words, they were fat. You could see it in every gallery in the land. Titian's voluptuous ladies. Ruben's gorgeously plentiful creatures – these were not ladies who followed the F-plan, nor wanted to.

That has been the accepted view – until now. Professor John Garrow is a nutritionist and editor of *The European Journal of Clinical Nutrition*.

He has cast an eye over the world's classical paintings. Rather than guessing whether the women Botticelli and Tintoretto painted are fat or thin, he has applied a mathematical measure of obesity to them. And his conclusion?

Painters over the centuries depicted thin models just as often as fat ones. He announced it in a lecture at Bart's Hospital, London, this week, saying: 'It isn't true that being thin is a modern phenomenon.'

The ideal weight for a woman – or a man – depends, among other things, on their height. Nutritionists measure obesity – fatness – by a mathematical calculation known as Body Mass Index, or BMI.

To get it from a painting, he estimates the weight of the woman depicted and divides it by the square of her height.

A BMI of 20 to 25 is the right ratio of height to weight for good health. A woman whose BMI is 18 or less is too thin for her own good. A BMI of 30 or more means that she is unhealthily overweight.

Professor Garrow found that the wonderfully shapely woman in Tintoretto's 1555 painting Susanna Bathing has a BMI of 29 – any fatter and she would be obese. But he also looked at Cranach the Elder, who

painted in the same era. The Eve in his Adam and Eve has a BMI of 19, making her barely fatter than waif-model Kate Moss.

'It is an interesting point,' says colleague Professor Andrew Hill. 'People tend to speak of the Middle Ages and Renaissance as times when the ideal female figure was generous. But there are other examples of quite lean figures.'

Durer's etchings tend to show elongated women. Botticelli's The Birth of Venus (1484) is round but not overweight and has long legs – which makes balancing on that rather unstable scallop shell even more difficult. Nutritionist Amanda Ursell estimated her BMI as 25 – not fat, just curvy. Parmigianino painted women like graceful straws. His The Madonna of the Long Neck (1535) has a BMI of around 22. It has been claimed that fatness was a sign of wealth, to be flaunted in portraiture, since only the rich got enough to eat. But medieval tapestries show courtly women, none of whom are fat, with a BMI of 19 or 20 for many of them. 'Perhaps a greater variety of figures were painted then, compared to today when only the very thinnest get their photographs in the fashion magazines,' says Professor Hill.

Also, an artist commissioned to paint a portrait had no option but to make it lifelike – and fat, if that's how the lady was.

I HEAR THAT SHE'S ON A STRICT DIET – ONLY ONE SCALLOP A DAY

Certainly desired body images for women have changed through the ages. The Willendorf Venus, one of the earliest known sculptures in the world, dates from the Palaeolithic age, and shows a woman who is almost spherical and clearly meant to be an object of desire. Her BMI? 'Almost off the scale,' says Amanda Ursell.

Medieval statues of the Virgin show a small head, small round breasts, big round belly thrust forward. That body shape became, it seems, the desired norm for women. The belly, of course, was not fat, but child-bearing. Yet even in the 16th century, slimness was desired – and not solely to please men. Catherine de Medici insisted that her ladies at

---

Every woman in the country thinks she is too large round the waist. Thin is beautiful. But has it always been so? Have women always wanted to be thin?

---

court had waists of, at most, 23 inches.

Tastes change and in pictures very often we see what we want to see. Manet was accused of pornography for painting his 1863 Olympia – not because she was nude,

but because she was thin. Even so, she is certainly not anorexic, which may be why her thinness does not seem obvious to us today. Her BMI would be around 23.

'It would seem hard to conclude that women of the past were either thinner or fatter than today. Perhaps it is just that they were less obsessed with their weight. Dieting as a mass obsession is something that only began after the Second World War.

'There is a lot of biased reporting, some of it by feminists, that the modern ideal of slender womanhood is something got up by male doctors and others,' said Professor Garrow in his lecture. 'It just is not so.'

© *The Daily Mail*
May, 1996

Anorexia of a taunted six-year-old

Girl starved herself to 2·5 stone after 'Blobby' jibes

By Angela Mollard

Watching Bobbie Beadle joke and play with her big brothers, no one would have guessed anything was wrong.

The six-year-old had lost weight, but her mother and the family GP put it down to childish eating fads.

It was only when Teresa Beadle heard her daughter telling friends she was fat that she realised the horrifying truth – Bobbie had an eating disorder.

Taunted by other children who dubbed her Blobby, the youngster started making herself sick after school lunches. At home, she would secretly dump her evening meal in the bin or sneak it on to her brothers' plates.

Finally her weight dropped to a distressing two and a half stone.

'I couldn't believe it when she told me she was fat,' Mrs Beadle said yesterday. 'There was my pretty little baby believing what two boys at her after-school club had told her.' She tried to persuade Bobbie to eat by making special treats, but she

continued to refuse. Some days she would have little more than a piece of toast and half a packet of crisps.

It was only when she saw her daughter having a bath that Mrs Beadle realised she needed professional help.

'I could see every bone sticking out under her skin,' she recalled. 'I had seen a TV programme on anorexia in a girl of 11 and I remembered thinking how young she was, but there was my six-year-old with the same thing.'

Mrs Beadle, from Abbey Wood, South-East London, took Bobbie to Greenwich Hospital where a paediatrician confirmed her fears. 'The doctor was concerned about how underweight she was. She said if she was two pounds lighter she would have to go into hospital.'

The mother was given nutritional advice and told to keep a diary of what her daughter ate each

day. Slowly Bobbie's weight climbed and she began to fit the pretty dresses and tops her mother had bought a year earlier.

'At first she couldn't keep her food down,' said Mrs Beadle, a 27-year-old divorcee. 'She would feel sick as soon as she ate anything.'

Six months on Bobbie, now seven, has put on a stone and no longer creeps out to the kitchen to scrape her meals into the bin.

Pat Fisher, Bobbie's head teacher at De Lucy School in Abbey Wood, said staff are keeping an eye on her and ensuring she eats lunch properly.

This week Mrs Beadle launched a support group for the parents of children suffering from eating disorders. 'There's plenty of advice and help available for teenagers, but nothing for younger children,' she said. 'As a child I never thought about my weight, but young girls these days are very conscious of how they look.'

© *The Daily Mail*
May, 1996

Caraline's lifeline

Involvement in volunteering can happen in unusual ways. Karen Gordon reports on how one young woman turned her personal experience of anorexia into voluntary work helping people with eating disorders. This subsequently became a full-time job

This year has been a particularly busy one so far for Claire Beeken. The 25-year-old from Luton runs Caraline, a helpline and self-help group providing counselling and support for people with anorexia nervosa and bulimia. The group was named after a close friend of Claire's who died of anorexia.

Originally Claire, who has had anorexia since she was 12, organised Caraline on a voluntary basis in her spare time. Her efforts were rewarded when she was presented with the Young Individual Award in the 1994 Whitbread Volunteer Action Awards. She has also received a BTEC certificate in counselling for her work. She has now given up her job with Radio Rentals to work full-time on the project.

Since starting Caraline a year ago Claire has helped over one hundred and fifty people of all ages, the youngest being 8. Many of these have been referrals from local consultants and doctors and the Eating Disorders Association.

She runs one-to-one counselling sessions and holds regular discussion groups for people with anorexia or bulimia. Claire also runs a carers group for the parents of people with eating disorders. 'It's important they get support too. It doesn't help the situation to have confrontations at meal times, and it's no use parents saying to an anorexic that they cannot leave the table until they've eaten everything. Everyone needs someone to talk to. The different groups complement each other quite nicely.'

Her work also involves giving talks in schools and colleges about what it's like to be anorexic. 'At first there's a silence from the audience, then questions about what should they do. I tell them to remember that food and weight are not the issue. It's best not to tell people how they look – look at them inside and tell them they look sad. Young girls ring up for information, saying they are doing a project on anorexia or bulimia, and I sometimes wonder why they have chosen those subjects. Perhaps it's a way of asking for help.'

> *Claire Beeken estimates that there are around 100,000 registered anorexics and bulimics, and that many of them die from the condition*

Claire Beeken estimates that there are around 100,000 registered anorexics and bulimics, and that many of them die from the condition. 'It has the highest mortality rate in psychiatric units,' she explains. 'Over 10 per cent of anorexics and bulimics die, either from the effects of starvation or by committing suicide.

'People tend to blame Kate Moss, but dieting doesn't mean someone's going to get anorexia. It's not a 'slimmer's disease', it's a way of coping. It blocks off their problems. Many people who have anorexia have been abused. People with anorexia or bulimia have very low self-esteem. I try to help build up their self-esteem and confidence.'

Claire has now secured funding for three years from the local health authority. Future funding permitting, Claire hopes to take on an administrative worker, and expand the carers group and bulimic programme. She would also like to start an open house for those with eating disorders. She acknowledges she will have to work hard on fundraising when the money from the health authority ends.

The intense publicity surrounding famous people with eating disorders, such as the Princess of Wales and Countess Spencer, has led to renewed and increased awareness of eating disorders, and growing demands on services such as Caraline.

Although Caraline covers the Buckinghamshire, Bedfordshire and Hertfordshire area, Claire gets calls from all over the country. 'I talk to them and refer them to their local EDA group,' explains Claire. 'It takes a lot of courage for someone to go to their doctor in the first place. Caraline gives them someone to talk to. It's sad it's so busy,' she concedes.

● Claire Beeken can be contacted at Caraline, 211 Hitchin Road, Luton, Bedfordshire LU2 UEP. Caraline Helpline on 01582 457474.

● The Eating Disorders Association is a membership organisation which publishes a number of booklets on anorexia nervosa and bulimia nervosa. It coordinates a network of self-help groups, and provides information and advice for people with eating disorders and their friends and families. Eating Disorders Association, Sackville Place, 44 Magdalen Street, Norwich NR3 2JE. Tel: 01603 621414. The EDA National Youth Helpline is on 01603 765050.

Eating disorders

Anorexia nervosa
Symptoms often include: severe weight loss; distortions and misconceptions about weight and body size; excessive exercising; isolation; emotional, irritable behaviour; difficulty in sleeping; and loss of menstrual periods.

Bulimia nervosa
Characterised by binge eating followed by self-induced vomiting, sufferers often move to bulimia from anorexia. Symptoms often include: disappearing to the lavatory after meals in order to get rid of food eaten; secretive behaviour; feeling out of control, helpless and lonely; and emotional behaviour and mood swings.

© Young People Now
July, 1995

Quiz

● Are you a binge-eater, a bulimic or just ordinary?
● Do you need to take action?
● To find out, read the following statements and note on a separate piece of paper your answers for each question. Choose your answers from Seldom, Sometimes, or Often. Choose the answer which is the most nearly true for you.

1   I eat when I am upset.
2   I feel insecure about myself.
3   I eat differently when I am with other people.
4   I weigh myself.
5   I feel I could be happy if I lost half a stone.
6   I binge and I feel I am losing control over stopping.
7   I know exactly what is in the fridge.
8   I am depressed.
9   My parents did not like me to make my own decisions.
10 I feel fat.
11 I have no confidence sexually.
12 Food controls my life.
13 I take laxatives.
14 I feel that other people are better than I am.
15 I drink too much alcohol.
16 My mother made me feel I was not needed.
17 My periods come at odd times.
18 I eat in secret.
19 My mother did not understand me.
20 I know the calorie value of what I am eating.
21 I am on a diet.
22 I think about food.
23 I make myself sick to control my weight.
24 If I eat one piece I have to go on until I finish the lot.
25 I feel empty inside emotionally.
26 I get an impulse to steal things in shops.
27 My life is out of control.
28 I think my stomach is too big.
29 I am afraid of getting fatter and fatter.
30 I think no one really likes me.

Scoring

For every Seldom, score 0; for every Sometimes, score 1; for every Often, score 2.

Your score

0-15   You have nothing to worry about.
15-30 You are becoming a binge-eater. Review your relationships and life-style.
30-45 You have developed bulimia and need treatment. Discuss this with your family doctor.
45+   Urgent – you need expert professional help as soon as possible.

● The above quiz is an extract from *How to cope with Bulimia*, by Dr Joan Gomez, published by Sheldon Press, priced at £5.99.

© Sheldon Press

Bulimia – a boy's own story

Eating disorders only affect girls, right? *Wrong.* Some guys also go to extremes to be model-thin and, as LOOKS found out, your boyfriend or brother could be a victim . . .

Daniel, a 22-year-old student, had never been happy with his weight. Four years ago, he developed bulimia nervosa and the pounds began to drop off. But that's when his problems really began – for the next two years he was caught in a vicious circle of starving, bingeing and vomiting.

'I always felt I had a weight problem. While the other kids at school grew out of their puppy fat, mine stayed with me. During my teens I became paranoid about my looks: at 5ft 5, I was short and at 10 stone looked pretty fat.

'It wasn't just my weight that got me down. I had no confidence when it came to girls, and I also felt really stupid compared to my three sisters. No matter how hard I worked, I couldn't compete with their grades at school. I always seemed to be letting my parents down and felt like a complete loser.

'The final straw came when I failed my A-levels, and had to watch my twin sister swan off to university. The stress of revising had taken its toll – I came down with glandular fever and lay in bed for six weeks – it was one of the worst periods of my life.

'Once I was well again, people started saying how good I was looking. I examined myself in the mirror – during the illness I'd dropped from 10 to eight stone, and I *did* look better for it.

'OK, I wasn't clever like my sisters, but my weight was one area of my life I could control. Instead of dieting, I started exercising like a maniac until I felt like I'd worked off what I'd eaten that day. I'd run up and down the stairs until I was on the verge of collapsing. I also joined a gym and spent hours working out.

'I had no idea that muscle weighs more than fat, so when my weight started to creep up again, I felt really depressed and defeated. It was around this time when I was house-sitting for my aunt, that I had my first eating binge. I hadn't eaten all day, so I was starving. I began with a Mars Bar, quickly followed by two Snickers. By this stage I was feeling totally out of control, I just couldn't stop myself. I ended up eating crisps, cake, doughnuts, cereal and ice cream – just about anything I could find. As I was stuffing the food into my mouth I caught sight of my reflection in the window. I was eating with the desperation of someone who hadn't eaten all week. I looked sad, pathetic and disgusting.

'I wasn't clever like my sisters, but my weight was one area of my life I could control'

'Within half an hour I'd eaten more than I had ever before in one go. I'd been a pig and hated myself for it. My stomach was bloated and I was sweating. I got up painfully and made my way to the bathroom, desperate to get rid of the food and the horrible choking feeling in my throat. I hunched over the toilet, rammed my fingers into my mouth over and over again and threw everything up.

'As I was being sick the horror of being out of control started to fade. I didn't realise I was forging the first link in a chain of starving, bingeing and vomiting.

'After that night it was a couple of weeks before I binged again. Pretty soon, though, the distances between binges got shorter and shorter. Within two months I was bingeing and then vomiting at least three times a day. It was my fix and I even started to enjoy it in a sad sort of way.

'Despite being bulimic, my weight never fell below eight stone. But as long as I threw up after eating, I felt I wouldn't get fat again.

'By the time I was 19, bulimia controlled my life. I couldn't eat without bingeing and then being sick. Every day was spent planning what I was going to eat. At meal times I'd secretly tip my food into the bin or feed it to the dog. I'd then go to my room, drag out my supply of junk food, stuff my face, then quietly throw up.

'Lying and stealing were part of my life. I'd even nick money from my parents to sustain my habit – I couldn't relax unless I had food ready for my next session.

'Amazingly, my family never suspected me. Then, when I'd been bulimic for almost two years, a family friend came to stay. He realised I was ill and confronted me. It was a relief to confess, though I knew he'd tell my parents. Understandably, they were horrified. Mum started reading up on bulimia and we went to see a counsellor who helped me work out why I'd become bulimic – low self-esteem was a big part of it. I also went on a sensible diet to help me get used to eating properly.

'Slowly, I overcame bulimia. For the first month I used alcohol as a means of escape, and this might have carried on if I hadn't decided to retake my A-levels. I threw myself into revising, so my mind was occupied.

'Although the two years when I had bulimia were horrific I don't feel like the black sheep of the family any more. My family are very proud of me and I'm doing well at university. My weight has stabilised at nine stone, and I'm coming to terms with my looks. Bulimia could have killed me, so my health is more of a priority than my image nowadays.'

© *LOOKS*
June, 1996

Help for parents and friends

Information from the Eating Disorders Association

Maybe you know someone who suffers from anorexia or bulimia nervosa and you are worried. The sufferer may perhaps be your child. Here are some suggestions from the Eating Disorders Association as to how you might understand and respond helpfully to the situation.

Anorexia and bulimia nervosa are outward signs that something is wrong inside. The problem really relates to a crisis about self-identity. Eating disorders provide a way of trying to reach a position of independence when this feels very difficult. Taking control of the body and food intake can seem perhaps the only way of achieving this. As parents or people close to a sufferer, you can be very helpful in this struggle. But it will not be easy for you! Parents can often feel that home has become a battleground with food as a very powerful weapon. It may seem as though conflicting messages come from the sufferer to the parents. It sometimes sounds like:

Leave me alone, let me live my own life, I hate you.

Don't ever leave me, I can't cope on my own, I love you.

This kind of ambivalence, these contradictory feelings are hard to live with. It is, however, important to allow these conflicting and painful emotions to be expressed. Periods of depression, anger, hopelessness and despair are all part of the experience of growing up. It is not easy for anyone concerned.

Parents too have feelings and may give out conflicting messages. It may sound like:

It must be all my fault. I'll do anything to make you better. I love you so much. I can't bear to see you so unhappy. I worry about you all the time. You are ruining my life. I want to shake you. At times I hate you.

Parents often end up feeling guilty and totally responsible for everything that has happened. This is not a good point from which to begin to tackle the problems presented by anorexia or bulimia nervosa.

Parents usually do what they think is best at the time, and everyone can be wise in retrospect. Accept what has happened in the past, and concentrate on what can be done now and in the future.

How can you help?

One of the barriers which sufferers have to overcome in order to get help with the problem is their own resistance to acknowledging that the problem is really very complex and there is no short cut to recovery.

You cannot make the sufferer overcome this barrier, but at least you need not collude with it and look for miracle cures.

Accept that at present this is the only way the sufferer feels that life is in control, the only way of coping.

- Be prepared to listen and give time.
- Accept that the sufferer will probably react badly to whatever approach you make – but don't let this put you off what you feel is right.
- The sufferer needs affirmation in every way and unconditional acceptance, not just for achievement.
- The sufferer needs to know that their company is valued, whether they eat or not.

- Don't leave lots of tempting goodies around or give extra or reduced helpings without being asked. Remember that the aim is to help the body eat what it really needs.
- Try to avoid confrontations over food.
- Seek professional help and persist if it is not forthcoming immediately.
- Read about the problems to increase your understanding.
- The idea of recovery can be frightening, so it is difficult for the sufferer to hear things like 'you look better', 'good, you've put on weight'.
- Her response to this sort of comment is likely to be 'I've put on weight – help – if I don't lose it again quickly I'll get fat'.
- Develop trust and friendship by being open and honest.
- Anorexia and bulimia nervosa are problems that affect not only the sufferer but the whole family and the circle which surrounds the sufferer.
- Try to continue living your own life as much as possible. Don't let the illness rule your life too. Look after your own needs and desires. You are entitled to your feelings. If you are to encourage the sufferer to express feelings openly and honestly, start off by setting an example.
- Accept that the character changes are part of the illness. The sufferer may become deceitful or start shoplifting. She needs help rather than to be judged.
- Progress may mean difficulties between parents and sufferer because it will involve a more assertive attitude and a degree of separation. This will be a struggle for all of you. It may be a

temporary period of difficulty whilst changes are being made. You may feel that you, as well as the sufferer, need some counselling or other help with your own feelings. Don't be afraid to ask. Progress requires change.

For the men in the family

The sufferer and the rest of the family need your help. Don't opt out by thinking that this is women's work. Try to share your feelings, ideas, work

Eating Disorders Association provides support for families and friends as well as sufferers. Most families find it helpful to talk with other families in a similar situation. Many of our groups also run separate groups for relatives and friends, and our telephone help-lines enable you to talk someone who understands eating disorders.

and leisure with the rest of the family. Accept them as equals and respect

their views so that they feel happy sharing their experiences with you too.

Useful literature

Anorexia Nervosa, by R.L. Palmer, published by Penguin Books.
Families and how to survive them, by John Cleese and Robin Skynner, published by Methuen Paperbacks.
Anorexia and Bulimia – How to help, by Marilyn Duker & Roger Slade, published by Open University Press.

© Eating Disorders Association

Specialist eating disorders unit

From Charter Nightingale Hospital

Located within an entirely separate area of the Charter Nightingale Hospital in a relaxed and homely atmosphere, the Eating Disorders Unit provides specialist treatment for patients suffering from Anorexia Nervosa, Bulimia Nervosa and Compulsive Overeating

Treatment on the Unit has been developed and continually refined to include the latest psychological techniques and ensures that patients receive the maximum therapy in the shortest possible time.

Therapy is available on an in-patient, day patient and out-patient basis and is provided by a skilled, multi-disciplinary team of clinicians supervised by the patient's Consultant Psychiatrist.

Aims of the treatment process
- To develop an understanding of the reasons why eating disorders occur.
- To establish and maintain a healthy weight and relationship with food.
- To identify and develop coping strategies for long term recovery.
- To raise self-esteem and confidence.

Assessment

Initially, an appointment is offered, free of charge, with a trained nurse counsellor to establish the patient's

specific needs and discuss the various treatment options available appropriate to their condition. Many patients also wish to meet the treatment team and tour the Unit at this time.

The initial appointment is normally followed by a formal assessment with a Consultant Psychiatrist, during which time an individualised treatment plan is agreed with the patient and, if appropriate, their family.

The treatment plan may include a spell of in-patient care and/or day care or a series of out-patient appointments with a Consultant Psychiatrist or Counsellor experienced in working with patients with eating disorders.

Treatment

Patients who are admitted for in-patient care or day care will access a core treatment programme which is largely group-orientated but also incorporates individual and family therapy. The following groups form an integral part of the treatment programme:
– Feelings group
– Self-awareness group

– Drama group
– Women's group
– Diet management
– Art therapy
– Assertion training
– Transactional analysis
– Family group
– Exercise and relaxation

Accommodation

The Unit provides 12 tastefully furnished bedrooms, a dining room/kitchen and group room.

Patients who wish to remain on the Unit may do so, however, generally they will be encouraged to make use of the Hospital dining room and recreation facilities.

Follow-up

In-patients will be followed up with out-patient appointments following discharge, however attendance as a day patient is normally encouraged.

In addition, a weekly support group is provided free of charge for patients, and their families, to help maintain long term recovery.

Should you wish further information about the Eating Disorders Unit or would like to arrange a confidential and free initial appointment with a Nurse Counsellor, please contact the Intake Department on: 0171 258 3828 (24 hours).

© Charter Nightingale Hospital

Eating problems

Information from ChildLine

Many young people experience difficulties with eating and food at some time in their lives. These can range from not liking certain foods (which happens to most people), to serious eating problems which may be medical and/or emotional in origin. 2% of young women and 0.2% of young men are affected by anorexia and bulimia, but about 10% of teenage girls suffer from eating disorders, although some of them have it in a very mild form. In 1994/95, 312 young people spoke to ChildLine counsellors about an eating problem: 304 girls and 8 boys. Of the 250 children who gave their age, 39 were 16 years old, 47 were 15 years old, 58 were 14 years old, and 48 13 years old. Children as young as 10 and 11 also phoned to talk about eating disorders.

What are the most common eating problems?

Anorexia nervosa
People with anorexia nervosa avoid eating and lose a lot of weight. They often feel fat, even when they are very thin. They may use other ways of staying thin, such as taking laxatives (which is dangerous) or exercising too much. They can become very weak and without special help some may even die.

Bulimia nervosa
This is when people binge and then make themselves sick to get rid of the food. People with bulimia may not look overweight or underweight and may find it easy to hide their eating problems. Continuous bingeing and vomiting can eventually do serious damage to the body.

Compulsive eating
This is when people eat much more than their bodies need over a long period, or use food to comfort or

distract themselves. This can lead to being overweight and to serious medical problems.

How do eating problems begin?
Eating problems often start as a response to other problems, such as unhappiness in the family, school pressures, the death of someone close, child abuse, or a combination of these and other things.

Without help, the eating problem itself can get out of control. It can damage people's bodies and can leave them feeling bad about themselves and others, depressed and even suicidal.

Many young people deny their eating problem or try to keep it a secret. But the sooner they accept that they have a problem, the easier it is to help. Help can include anything from talking to friends, family or a confidential counsellor such as ChildLine, to seeing a doctor or spending time in hospital.

What do young people tell ChildLine about their eating problems?

- Sarah told a ChildLine counsellor that she started to eat a lot under the pressure of exams. She put on weight and this led to her being teased and called names. She became very embarrassed about her size and said that one of the things that helped most was to talk to someone who couldn't see her.

- Niri, 15, was doing well at school, had lots of friends and belonged to a drama group; then her family moved to another part of the country. Niri developed anorexia as a way of expressing how very upset she felt about the move.

- Jon phoned ChildLine over many months. He was having medical treatment for bulimia and the whole of his life felt out of control. He told ChildLine that he started bingeing and vomiting after he had been sexually abused. He said 'there is something bad inside me that I need to get out'. Jon said that talking to his ChildLine counsellor helped to feel more in control of his life and happier about himself.

How can ChildLine help?

- ChildLine counsellors listen without blaming or criticising. They take young people's problems seriously.
- It can be easier to talk on the phone than face to face, especially at first.
- Supportive family and friends are important, but it often helps to talk to someone who is not personally involved.
- Young people can write as well as phone, just once, or arrange to speak to the same counsellor over a period of time.
- ChildLine can talk to you about who else can help you with an eating problem.

If you need to talk in confidence about an eating problem, – or are worried about someone else with this problem – you can call ChildLine free, 24 hours a day, on 0800 1111, or write to ChildLine, Freepost 1111, London N1 0BR.

© *ChildLine*
January, 1996

INDEX

ADDITIONAL RESOURCES

You might like to contact the following organisations for further information. Due to the increasing cost of postage, many organisations cannot respond to enquiries unless they receive a stamped, addressed envelope.

Advertising Standards Authority
Brook House
Torrington Place
London WC1 7HJ
Tel: 0171 580 5555
Fax: 0171 631 3051

The ASA has published a report on slimming advertisements.

British Nutrition Foundation
High Holborn House
52-54 High Holborn
London WC1V 6RQ
Tel: 0171 404 6504
Fax: 0171 404 6747

An independent charity which provides reliable information and advice on nutrition and related health matters. They produce a wide range of leaflets, briefing papers and books. Ask for their publications list.

Charter Nightingale Hospital
11-19 Lisson Grove
London NW1 6SH
Tel: 0171 258 3828
Fax: 0171 724 6827

The hospital has an Eating Disorders Unit which provides specialist treatment for patients suffering from anorexia nervosa, bulimia nervosa and compulsive overeating.

ChildLine
2nd Floor Royal Mail Building
Studd Street
London N1 0QW
Tel: 0171 239 1000 (admin)
Fax: 0171 239 1001

Childline is the free, national helpline for children and young people in trouble or danger. It provides confidential phone counselling service for any child with any problem 24 hours a day. Children or young people can phone (Freephone 0800 11 11) or write (Freepost 1111) free of charge about problems of any kind.

Eating Disorders Association (EDA)
Sackville Place
44 Magdalene Street
Norwich NR3 1JU
Tel: 01603 664 915

A national charity set up to help people with anorexia and bulimia nervosa, their families and friends and those offering treatment. They offer a wide range of services including telephone helplines, useful factsheets and advice leaflets, a professional journal, and training courses for school nurses and other staff.
Telephone helpline: 01603 621414
Youth Helpline:(18 years and under): 01603 765 050
Recorded message: 0891 615 466 if you would like to listen to a recorded message about anorexia and bulimia nervosa.

Fat Women's Group
London Women's Centre
Wesley House
4 Wild Court
London WC2B 4AU
Tel: 0171 2817819

Celebrates fat women in all their diversity. Provides support for individual members. Campaigns politically against all forms of fat hatred and fat fear.

First Steps to Freedom
22 Randall Road
Kenilworth
Warwicks CV8 1JY
Tel: 01926 851608

Offers advice, support and counselling to people who suffer from phobias, general anxiety, obsessional compulsive disorders, and their carers. Produces publications.

Health Education Authority
Hamilton House
Mabledon Place
London WC2H 9TX

Tel: 0171 3833 833
Fax: 0171 387 0550

For information about their publications list phone Customer Service on 01235 465565

MIND
Granta House
15-19 Broadway
Stratford
London E15 4BQ
Tel: 0181 519 2122

MIND is a leading mental health charity in England and Wales. They produce a wide range of advice leaflets (45p each), reports and books.

National Food Alliance (NFA)
5-11 Worship Street
London, EC2A 2BH
Tel: 0171 628 2442
Fax: 0171 628 9329

A voluntary organisation for those interested in food and health from a public interest perspective. Produce a newsletter, briefing papers and reports.

Schools Health Education Unit
University of Exeter
Heavitree Road, Exeter
Devon EX1 2LU
Tel: 01392 264 722

Publish *Young People in 1994*, which summarises the results of a survey of carried out in 279 schools in England and Scotland. The survey covers a wide range of issues.

Young Minds
102-108 Clerkenwell Road
London, EC1M 5SA
Tel: 0171 336 8445
Fax: 0171 336 8446

Young Minds, the national association for children's mental health. Produces a range of leaflets, reports, a magazine and newsletters.

ACKNOWLEDGEMENTS

The publisher is grateful for permission to reproduce the following material.

While every care has been taken to trace and acknowledge copyright, the publisher tenders its apology for any accidental infringement or where copyright has proved untraceable. The publisher would be pleased to come to a suitable arrangement in any such case with the rightful owner.

Chapter One: Watching your weight

Are you a healthy weight?, © Health Education Authority, *Weight*, © The Flora Project for Heart Disease Prevention, June 1995, *Fear of fat*, © Essentials, April 1996, *Your ideal weight*, © New Woman, January 1996, *Call for radical rethink on treatment of obesity*, © The Telegraph plc, London 1996, *Attention all dieters: now you can eat what you like*, © The Independent, May 1996, *Slim chance . . .*, © SHE Magazine, June 1996, *Food for thought*, © The Guardian, May 1996, *Fatty issue sparks food protest*, © The Independent, April 1996, *The key to slimming without pain*, © The Telegraph plc, London 1995, *Britons urged to walk themselves fitter*, © The Independent, March 1996, *Why slimming ads are bad for health*, © National Food Alliance Project, March 1996, *Television 'feeds children diet of junk food'*, © The Telegraph plc, London 1995, *Danger drugs freely given to all who ask*, © The Independent, April 1996, *Fatty puffs*, © The Economist, May 1996, *Weight on their minds*, © The Daily Mail, March 1996.

Chapter Two: Eating disorders

Understanding eating distress, © MIND 1995, *Did you know . . .*, © Eating Disorders Association, *'A New Year diet triggered my anorexia'*, © More!, 3-16 January 1996, *Helping a friend or a relative*, © Eating Disorders Association, *Breaking the chains of eating disorders*, © Here's Health, January 1996, *Is the Kate Moss look really 500 years old?*, © The Daily Mail, November 1995, *Anorexia of a taunted six-year-old*, © The Daily Mail, November 1995, *Caraline's lifeline*, © Young People Now, July 1995, *Quiz*, From *How to cope with Bulimia*, © Sheldon Press, *Bulimia – a boy's own story*, LOOKS, June 1996, *Help for parents and friends*, © Eating Disorders Association, *Specialist eating disorders unit*, © Charter Nightingale Hospital, *Eating problems*, ChildLine, January 1996.

Photographs and Illustrations

Pages 2, 12: Katherine / Folio Collective, pages 5, 30: Andrew Smith / Folio Collective, pages 9, 14, 19, 23: Ken Pyne, pages 20, 28: Anthony Haythornthwaite / Folio Collective, pages 25, 32 Ralf Ziegermann.

Craig Donnellan
Cambridge
September, 1996